JOHN H. DAVIS AND
KENNETH HINSHAW

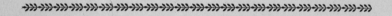

FARMER
in a Business Suit

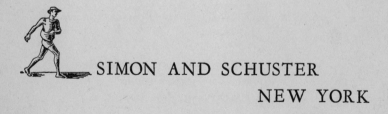

SIMON AND SCHUSTER
NEW YORK

First Printing

LIBRARY OF CONGRESS CATALOG CARD NUMBER: 57-7308

MANUFACTURED IN THE UNITED STATES OF AMERICA
PAPER COVERED EDITION BOUND
BY SENDOR BINDERY, INC., NEW YORK, N. Y.

ACKNOWLEDGMENTS

➤➤➤➤➤➤➤➤➤➤➤➤➤➤➤➤➤➤➤➤➤➤➤➤➤➤➤➤➤➤➤➤➤➤➤

The authors express their sincere appreciation to the Harvard University Graduate School of Business Administration, whose study of agribusiness has served as a basis for this book. Particularly helpful has been the co-operation of Ray Goldberg, co-author of the Harvard study.

The authors also wish to thank the Foundation for American Agriculture for the unstinting support it has given them in connection with the research and writing involved in the creation of this book. The Foundation's Board of Directors comprises:

James A. McConnell, Cornell University, Chairman
William T. Brady, Corn Products Refining Company, Vice Chairman
John Collyer, B. F. Goodrich Company, Vice Chairman
Edward E. Woolman, Hales and Hunter, Secretary-Treasurer
Tobin Armstrong, Rancher
Crowdus Baker, Sears, Roebuck and Company
Homer Brinkley, National Council of Farmer Cooperatives
Clark L. Brody, Farm Bureau Services, Inc.

v

ACKNOWLEDGMENTS

E. G. Cherbonnier, Agricultural Business Consultant
Thomas L. Daniels, Archer-Daniels-Midland Company
John H. Davis, Harvard Graduate School of Business
Victor Emanuel, Avco Manufacturing Corporation
Walter D. Fuller, Curtis Publishing Company
F. Peavey Heffelfinger, F. H. Peavey and Company
Earl M. Hughes, Farmer
Porter M. Jarvis, Swift and Company
John L. McCaffrey, International Harvester Company
John M. Marble, Rancher
Albert Mitchell, Rancher
Herschel Newsom, The National Grange
Graham Patterson, *Farm Journal*
John W. Scott, Farmer
Robert S. Stevenson, Allis-Chalmers Manufacturing Company
A. L. Strand, Oregon State College
R. Douglas Stuart, Quaker Oats Company
Francis Wilcox, Sunkist Growers
W. G. Wysor, Southern States Cooperative, Inc.

Of particular help was the encouragement, counsel and assistance of Charles Dana Bennett, special consultant to the Foundation for American Agriculture. Valuable encouragement and aid were also provided by John Strohm, agricultural editor and writer.

JOHN H. DAVIS
KENNETH HINSHAW

CONTENTS

꧁꧂꧁꧂꧁꧂꧁꧂꧁꧂꧁꧂꧁꧂꧁꧂꧁꧂꧁꧂꧁꧂꧁꧂꧁꧂꧁꧂꧁꧂꧁꧂꧁꧂꧁꧂

INTRODUCTION

This book is a human-interest story of one of the most important economic developments in American history—the transition from the self-sufficient farming of the old homestead to the modern combination of agriculture and business that now provides our great abundance of food and fiber. The farmer in a business suit personifies agribusiness—a new and stimulating concept of economics relating to and including modern agriculture.

Agribusiness itself is a dynamic proposition, since it includes all those factors both on and off the farm which are involved in the production, processing and distribution of food and fiber. The bigness of our present agribusiness economy is breathtaking—ninety of the 248 billion dollars of our 1955 national consumption expenditures. But there is more to agribusiness than its status in terms of dollars at any given time. Agribusiness is an important form of progress—a continuing evolution in technology, science and business that makes farming and its products ever more useful. Agribusiness presents both challenges and opportunities in forming our farm, busi-

ness and governmental policies. It is a new approach to all the decisions farmers and businessmen make in providing the greatest use, the most desirable satisfactions from our food and fiber resources. It is the framework within which the only effective solution for the chronic farm problem can be found.

Farmer in a Business Suit *is the flesh-and-blood story of people engaged in agribusiness—the businessmen whose enterprises supply sixteen billion dollars' worth of supplies for farms . . . the farmers whose productive operations are a fourteen-billion-dollar service . . . and the businessmen whose transporting, storing, processing and merchandising operations account for sixty billion to swell the agribusiness total to its ninety-billion mark.*

The farmer in a business suit has taken the place of the old homesteader. His horsepower is bred in factories and his stock is fed by the white-frocked scientists in the laboratories that produce those fabulous substances known as antibiotics and hormones. His family farm is a costly, efficient, revved-up complex of fields, barns and equipment with a gluttonous hunger for capital and managerial know-how. His productivity is a hundred, a thousand times his family's own needs. His harvests flow through myriads of enterprises and arrive in your kitchen cleaned, prepared and processed as if by built-in maid service.

How the farmer in a business suit struggles for his place in the modern scheme of things . . . how he lives . . . what he's thinking . . . and how he'll influence your own way of life: that's what this book sets out to tell you.

Part One

THE EARTHBOUND ERA

⇛⇛⇛⇛⇛⇛⇛⇛⇛⇛⇛⇛⇛⇛⇛⇛⇛⇛⇛⇛⇛⇛⇛⇛⇛⇛⇛⇛⇛⇛⇛⇛

For three centuries the significance of American agriculture was such that it could be described as a great frontier. Part of this frontier was in the land itself—the wild, new land which pioneers moving westward could settle and convert to productive farms and ranches. Another part of this frontier was in the economic progress of the period—the opportunity for farm families to develop a highly satisfactory standard of living, even a comparatively prosperous way of life, out of the resources within the fence lines of their farms. This was the period when farming was a major occupation and agriculture's product was a major segment of the nation's economy. Some of the businesses which furnish supplies for farming or handle, process and market products originating on farms had already appeared. They grew in size, numbers and versatility—but they were a much smaller part of the total economy than was agriculture. During the Earthbound Era, their development was not sufficiently important to give birth to the agribusiness idea. Instead, the frontier where men could seek opportunity based on agriculture was thought to be bound to land . . . its possession and its use.

1.

A GOOD PLACE to begin this story is in Massachusetts Bay Colony in the year 1633. A Puritan colonist named John Yeoman * owned some hogs that rooted a big, ugly hole alongside a section of the pine poles that fenced his hog pen. John was a busy man and he didn't take the time to place a large stone or a heavy log in the pit his porkers were excavating. Then one day the hogs joyfully discovered their rooting had opened a gateway to the world outside their pen. They promptly began to explore the neighborhood. Of particular interest was a settler's patch of Indian corn, the most wonderful spot on earth in the opinion of a hungry hog.

But it was a spree like this that led to trouble. Owners of

* Meaning a cultivator of his own land; a freeman.

corn patches had suffered aplenty from the wanderlust of errant hogs, and Puritan tongues were grimly restrained from expressing profanely how it feels to have one's tasseled corn ravaged by a horde of bristled bandits. But, alas, John's swine chose a magistrate's garden for the scene of their mischief. Now a magistrate was a man to be reckoned with respectfully. He was commissioned by the Massachusetts Bay Colony to serve as an early version of the hard-boiled ranch foreman. When something made him sore, woe to the unfortunate Puritan who was a party to his peeve.

John's magistrate didn't stop at stoning his neighbor's pigs out of the corn patch, nor was it enough that he scolded John roundly for letting the pigs escape. This magistrate convened with his fellow bossmen and they declared it "lawful for any man to kill any swine that comes into his corn."

"That's outrageous!" exclaimed John when he heard of the declaration.

Three hundred years ago a hog was an important part of a family's food supply during the long months between the frosts that killed the settler's garden and the warm days of summer that matured his early vegetables. For a hog to be killed midway in its growth was, therefore, a calamity of considerable dimensions . . . and John Yeoman and many other Puritans who owned hogs didn't like the idea at all.

They passed the word around and persuaded the hog owners in each town to choose two delegates to attend a meeting . . . and this was reportedly the first convention of record called on the continent of North America. When John Yeoman and his fellow pork growers assembled, they demanded that they be shown the royal charter. To their satisfaction, they saw that the making of laws rested with the freemen, not the magistrates. So . . . if there were to be laws concerning trespassing pigs, the freemen themselves would do the making.

Now this was an awesome proposition. Not only was lawmaking in their hands but also money-raising power was theirs, too. Solemnly they scrapped the magistrates' edict that an outraged corn grower could use his blunderbuss on a neighbor's vagabond hogs, and concluded furthermore that they ought to meet again next year and get on with some lawmaking and money-raising according to the privileges provided for them in the colony's charter. That next meeting established the general court, the beginning of our American form of representative government.

John Yeoman lived at the end of a trail, marked by blazed trees, leading through the virgin forest of eastern Massachusetts. His home was built of logs, notched where they met at the corners, and roofed with thatch. It stood in an old Indian clearing, encircled by a high palisade which also protected his cattle shed and the spring that provided water for his family and his livestock. At one end there was a large chimney built of stone cemented with clay. The small windows were covered with oiled paper and protected by shutters. John's door was thick and rugged. Both the floor and ceiling were made of riffed or split pine. The ceiling above the ground floor provided a floor for the loft. Skillful use of an adze had smoothed the surfaces of the interior and countless footsteps had worn away the softer parts of the flooring, leaving bumps where the hard knots resisted wear. Beneath the floor there was a deep, small cellar walled with stone. Sand had been tamped into its earth floor, and, stocked or empty, the odor of turnips, potatoes, apples and smoked meat saturated its cool atmosphere. A broad, stone hearth extended across most of the wall where the chimney was constructed. There were no partition walls.

5

Heavy serge curtains were drawn into place at night to separate the beds arranged along the walls. The coverings for these were rugs, and flannel sheets.

Pieces of furniture were few but practical. One or maybe two high-back chairs, a massive table, a large chest with a pretentious carved front, some birch-bark boxes made by Indian craftsmen for storing clothing, a large dresser used as cupboard and sideboard—these items sufficed to give the colonist and his family the comforts of home.

John Yeoman's food was frugal and wholesome. Porridge for breakfast; bread, cheese and beer or cider for luncheon; one of these—a boiled dish, black broth, salt fish, broiled pork, baked beans—for dinner; hasty pudding and milk for supper. Swedish turnips were the staple vegetable. Bread was made of corn, barley or rye meal. John's wife took pride in making berry and fruit pies, and for her to be able to comment, not to say boast, that any meal from breakfast to supper had been embellished by a pie created from the season's prime pie-making resource was gratifying in the extreme. Cooked food was prepared at the open hearth in cast-iron vessels suspended over the coals from metal arms pivoting on the sturdy andirons. It was served in wooden bowls and trenchers, earthen platters and horn drinking cups. John's pewter tankard was the symbol of a man of property. And on the broad mantel, flanked by a cresset lamp and an hourglass, rested a well-thumbed Bible.

John's wife, Patricia, was his helpmate. In addition to producing a big brood of youngsters, she was the family dairy operator, the laundress, mender and seamstress. She carded wool; did the spinning, weaving and knitting that provided bedding, rugs and clothing for the family. If Indians attacked, she was the ordnance department and quartermaster corps that kept ammunition, food and water ready while John manned the family matchlock.

"How much may be said of the part that woman played, or rather 'worked,' in the grand drama of our first settlements!" wrote Rev. Charles Brooks. "What would our Pilgrim Fathers have been without our Pilgrim Mothers? Women dared to follow where man dared to lead; and she brought with her the sanctifying power of true religion. She came to this wilderness with a brave heart and a Christian faith, that she might share the perils and brighten the hopes of her husband; and, when here, she looked well to the ways of her household, and ate not of 'the bread of idleness.' "

During the next hundred years, the descendants of Puritans like John and Patricia Yeoman developed a colonizing technique that planted settlements in the wilderness surrounding the Bay colony. Those wishing to establish themselves in New Hampshire, Vermont and Maine could apply for a grant to give them possession of a new area. This grant prescribed that the church and the schoolhouse were to be made an integral part of the new community, with each settler's family responsible to share equitably in the support of both. Here, for instance, are the conditions on which settlement of a New Hampshire town was authorized in 1732:

> That within the space of four years . . . they settle and have on the spot 81 families; each settler to build a good convenient dwelling house, one story high, 18 feet square at least; and fence, clear and bring to, four acres fit for improvement; and three acres more well stocked with English grass; and also to lay out three shares throughout the town, each share to be $\frac{1}{84}$th part of said tract of land, one of said shares to be for the first settled minister, one for the ministry, and one for the school; and also

7

to build a convenient meeting house, and settle a learned orthodox minister . . .

These specifications are interesting because they reveal that
a thrifty family could make its living 200 years ago from four
"improved" acres, plus three acres of grass for livestock forage.

Apparently the typical colonial family followed an established pattern in making its livelihood and acquiring the possessions that improved its standard of living. Its first step was
to affiliate with an organization that made plans and arranged
for proper authority to settle a wilderness area. The immigrant
family outfitted itself in the old country, bringing with it the
heirlooms and keepsakes treasured perhaps for generations and
sheltering these along with essential tools and provisions in its
log cabin in the American wilderness. Similarly the venturesome family already transplanted to coastal America cast its
lot with an organized project to settle new territory, packed
up its possessions and moved westward. Some families were
prosperous, some were close to poverty, when they settled on
the frontier. Often the things they carried into the wilderness
were incongruous in the rustic environs of their new homes—
statuary and fine linens, worn old Bibles and elegant leather-
bound books by great authors, paintings and handsome sets of
silver and pewter, delicate china and ornate furniture, jewelry
and the tools that craftsmen use—strange things to find under
the same roof with bearskin rugs, racks of Indian corn, strings
of dried venison and buckskin footwear and clothing.

But whether a family brought much or little to embellish its
frontier home, its prospects depended mostly on the use it
could make of the new land it acquired. Home-grown food
was the essential for livelihood. Progress beyond that was erratic, subject more or less to the whims of circumstance. Some-

8

times the sale of such things as lumber, an accumulation of cattle or horses, or an uncommon product such as tobacco gave the settler a windfall of money that set him on the road to financial progress. Ordinarily, however, his family saw very little money—in fact, needed very little because the land could be used to provide nearly all the products that it consumed or that could be exchanged at the trading post for other essentials. To a great extent the early American family was self-sufficient —making its livelihood, increasing its possessions little by little—dependent on earthbound agriculture.

Changes in the mode of living for the Yeoman family were barely noticeable decade after decade for a span of two centuries. Clearings were extended, more homesites established, and the foot trails through the forests became wagon roads connecting farms and villages. Farming communities ceased to worry about Indian attacks, so the protective palisades were taken down and men and women worked in the woods and fields without bothering to keep a loaded flintlock within arm's reach. With bigger fields and more livestock, farm families no longer faced a desperate struggle to produce barely enough food for themselves. As the towns grew, the farmers round about managed to supply more and more products to feed and clothe the townspeople. Enterprising men put dams across the streams to harness water power for the mills they established to saw lumber and grind grain. Prospering farmers forsook their log homes and moved their families into handsome clapboard houses.

The best of these had a well-to-do look—like a substantial old gentleman who has settled down to live on the interest of his earnings. Many of them are community landmarks even today . . . their white clapboards, green shutters and beautifully balanced proportions as appealing to the eye now as any-

9

thing two centuries of architecture's progress has been able to offer us. Their charm was enhanced by utility of interiors as well as the appeal of outward beauty. The colonial farmhouse builders used a massive chimney, often with fireplaces on four sides, as the basic element of their designs. Front doors opened on convenient hallways with staircases featuring graceful banisters leading to second-floor chambers. The hallways gave admittance to large rooms on each side of the house— "best rooms" with small turkey carpets and cupboards displaying the good dames' china tea set on one side while "fore rooms" furnished with eight-day grandfather clocks, framed samplers and thick plate mirrors were on the other side. The most comfortable part of these houses, however, was the kitchen or "keeping room" occupying an ell back of the main structure. Low-ceilinged, with dingy, unpainted panelwork, this was where the family was most together. Here the fireplace was flanked by the great and little oven and the "settles" where youngsters cuddled. Here too was the family dye pot, the pickle firkin, the spit hooks that testified to good living. The corner cupboard gleamed with pewter and the tankards boasted constantly of the merit of each farm's cider. Off the kitchens were the cheese rooms, with shelves leaning under the weight of the products the womenfolk prepared.

One of John Yeoman's descendants, Daniel Yeoman—the namesake of that great farmer and statesman Daniel Webster— built just such a house in the Connecticut valley, completing it in 1825. Incidentally, although Daniel Webster will live in our memory for his famous oratory on topics of his day, his deathbed request was to have his farm hands drive his cattle slowly past his sickroom window so that he could appraise his accomplishments as a stockman in the last hours of his remarkable career. Well, Daniel Yeoman was one of many

Massachusetts farmers who became members of agricultural societies after they were started in 1792. The purpose of these organizations was to upgrade farming in all respects. This was no trifling proposition. Several of the greatest personalities of this period were closely identified with advancement in the science of farming. There was, above all, George Washington, the national hero, whose prime interest was to improve the agricultural practices on his beloved Mount Vernon. And there was Thomas Jefferson, the nation's third President, who earned a master farmer degree by his superior farming at Monticello. There was Andrew Jackson, who achieved notable farming success at Hermitage; John C. Calhoun, who did very well with a mountain farm; and Henry Clay, whose farming at Ashland was much admired. These were big names, for the most part backed up by considerable wealth, but what these prominent men were learning about farming, how they were operating their holdings and what results they were achieving received a great deal of attention. In many parts of the country, there was a notable inclination on the part of distinguished citizens to associate with progressive farmers in forming societies to promote interest in better farming. These groups gave recognition to outstanding farmers and provided forums in which agricultural leaders exchanged ideas and compared experiences. It was in this type of society that Daniel Yeoman enthusiastically participated.

In Massachusetts, farmers made up the active memberships, but many of the commonwealth's business leaders considered it a privilege to help support these undertakings and their contributions helped make bigger the prizes which the societies offered as incentives for improving agricultural practices. Recipients of these awards, more than a hundred years ago, produced one-acre yields that were, indeed, astounding—117 bushels of shelled corn (56 pounds to the bushel); 52 bushels of barley; 518 bushels of potatoes; 900 bushels of carrots; 783 bushels of beets; 651 bushels of onions; five tons of hay. In quest of one of the society's awards for general farming achievement, Daniel Yeoman made a report * to his county committee in the year 1856 and this is what he submitted:

The farm which I offer for the three years' premium contains 150 acres, 35 of which are out-lands of a very light, sandy soil, producing very light crops when they are subjected to tillage. The other portion lies in one body and is divided as follows: 10 acres are covered with a fine growth of young wood; 50 acres will be in pasture the coming season; eight or nine are stocked down to mowing; five or six are waste or swamp lands, and the remainder is sown with rye, while a few acres are reserved for oats.

The soil is principally a dark sandy loam, with a subsoil of sand, which is far from being retentive of manures. My attention is chiefly directed to the raising of grains, the most important of which are rye and Indian corn. Of the former, I usually sow, on an average, 16 acres, and plant of the latter about 30. I consider roots a very important article for feeding milch cows during the winter. And the great secret of successful farming is the making and saving of the greatest quantity of valuable manure, a secret which I think most farmers, myself among the number, have heretofore been ignorant of, or have grossly neglected.

My farm presents an even, or rather a very flat surface, and consequently I am somewhat troubled with the surface water in spring and fall; but all this, by proper draining, can be con-

* The statements and figures used here are from a report made in November 1856 by H. E. Mosely of Springfield, Massachusetts, to the Hampden County Agricultural Society.

ducted into a small stream which runs entirely across the farm. My buildings consist of a two-story house, 22 x 47 feet, with an ell; a barn, 40 x 50 feet, with cow-shed attached; a hog house and corn crib; a cart shed 24 x 36 feet. By stabling my cows at night during the summer, and throwing pond muck, or any other absorbent, under them each night, I find I am able to make as much manure, and of far more value, than I can make in winter. And now for the figures. The farm is found upon the assessors' books, valued at about $4000.

The interest of which is		$ 240.00
Invoice of stocks:		
At present I have two oxen, worth	$150.00	
2 horses	100.00	
2 cows, three years old	70.00	
4 steers, one and two years old	100.00	
4 old hogs and 4 pigs	70.00	
Interest on same		29.40
Amount paid for labor		126.00
My own labor		150.00
My wife's labor, with a girl's help a portion of the time		105.00
Blacksmith's bill and other items		25.00
Hay seed and plaster		16.00
Guano		9.62
Taxes		37.67
Expense of keeping stock		348.49
Rearing and fattening swine, sour milk and kitchen waste excepted		65.00
Estimated expense of supporting family of six persons		350.00
		———
TOTAL EXPENSE, WITH INTEREST ON FARM AND STOCK		$1,502.18

13

The produce of the farm is as follows:

300	bushels Indian corn	$ 300.00
200	bushels rye	200.00
125	bushels oats	62.50
200	bushels potatoes	100.00
16	bushels onions	12.00
76	bushels carrots	28.50
4	bushels beans	10.00
50	bushels turnips	12.50
6	tons hay	90.00
6	tons rye straw	50.00
2	tons oat straw	16.00
15	acres corn fodder	50.00
Beef sold		90.00
Pigs sold		40.00
Tobacco		300.00
Butter, 225 pounds		56.25
Five cartloads of pumpkins		10.00
One hundred heads of cabbage		4.00
Growth of stock		75.00
Pasturing		44.00
Labor done off the farm		250.00
Tobacco plants		⬤.00

TOTAL	$2,066.75
DEDUCT EXPENSES	1,502.18
NET PROFIT	$ 564.57

November, 1856

His land and the way he used it enabled Daniel Yeoman to make a good living for his wife and their four sons and two daughters. Joseph, the oldest son, progressed from childhood

14

chores to becoming a working partner with his father . . . and, in keeping with the traditions of their English ancestry, it was taken for granted that he would inherit the home farm and in time pass it on to his oldest son, God willing that he was to have a son or sons.

The younger Yeoman boys helped about the farm during their boyhood, but as they grew older they sought jobs in the near-by manufacturing villages. These opportunities blossomed from childhood visits to the homes of aunts, uncles and cousins who lived in the towns. Sometimes a visit lasted all winter and permitted the young nephew or cousin from the farm to attend the village school, or work in one of the shops where training in the mechanical trades was provided. These absences from the farm stretched to longer periods of town and village schooling or employment as the boys grew older. When jobs ran out, the young men returned temporarily to the home farm, often bringing some of their village companions with them for a holiday in the country. And these visitors provided the answer to the question: What was to be the future for the Yeomen daughters? Hay rides, sleigh rides, church socials, picnics and outings made ideal settings for the romances that came naturally . . . and thus the two daughters of Daniel Yeoman left the family homestead, one to become the bride of a young railroad brakeman, the other to marry a department-store clerk.

Abner, the youngest of Daniel's sons, was born in 1840. He got a job in a foundry when he was sixteen, but after four years of it he developed a severe cough which was aggravated by exposure to foundry fumes and the great ranges of temperature experienced in handling the molten metals. When the cough persisted, the family doctor warned that Abner was on the verge of consumption and that he should give up the foundry job and move to a warm, dry climate. Young Abner took the warning philosophically—California was warm and dry, and its gold fields offered a place to apply his interest in metallurgy.

He made part of the long, transcontinental trip by train, the rest of it by stage coach, marveling all the way at the vastness of the area over which the American people had spread their civilization. He saw plowmen turn the black, rich soil of Illinois . . . drovers trail their great herds of cattle over the hills of Missouri . . . lonesome "mule skinners" steering their freight wagons across the flat sea of Kansas grass that spread from horizon to horizon. He gazed at the settlers' shacks dotting this vast expanse where only a little while ago the Buffalo grazed in herds so big they covered more ground than most New England townships. He blinked in amazement at the huge bands of sheep feeding on the slopes of Colorado mountains . . . groaned as he passed through the vast wastes of sagebrush and sand hour after hour, day after day in the territories of Utah and Nevada. And he rejoiced, weary but happy, to find that his destination in California was amid forested hills that bordered rich and beautiful valleys.

Gold in California, young Abner soon learned, was rarely the product of bold, dazzling adventure in mountain mining camps. Instead, it came mostly from the sweat and skills a man could trade for wages in the bustling communities that served the farming and lumbering regions round about. Reluctantly, he forsook his dreams of finding ore from which his knowledge of metallurgy could wrest a fortune in the yellow metal, and settled himself to the practical task of carpentry, and thus engaged, he prospered while California settled its frontier ranch by ranch, town by town. But this was a departure from the plans Abner had in the back of his mind. True, he had responded eagerly to the occupational opportunities that existed in his foundry job, and he had quite willingly put aside any thought of a lifetime attachment to the home farm, but these outward attitudes were only a mask that covered his deep resolve someday to have good land of his own, with its fine, big white house overlooking his own green fields and orchards. Working in the foundry, seeking gold or building houses and stores in frontier towns were merely expedient measures taken to earn the money that could help him carry out his ambition to become a prosperous landowner.

When it was certain that California's warm, dry atmosphere had, indeed, restored Abner's health, he courted and married Margaret, the daughter of a Scotch immigrant. They made their home on the outskirts of a town in the heart of a farming valley, and Abner kept a cow and a flock of chickens, raised a big garden and planted berry bushes and fruit trees just to get his hand ready for the day he would give up his carpentry trade and become a man of agriculture.

While Abner and Margaret Yeoman were thus planning their future and saving the silver dollars that could make it possible, the terrible years of the War between the States passed and the difficulties of reconstruction disrupted the country's economy. Even in far-off California, farmers and townspeople felt the disturbing uncertainties that clouded the outlook year on year. It was not a good time to take rash ventures when a family could get along well enough within the limitations of its established way of life. With the birth of their first child, a daughter they named Mary, Abner and Margaret Yeoman took a more cautious view of their plans to buy an established farm in their locality or to seek a homestead claim somewhere on the frontier . . . and while they deliberated, their second child, little Benjamin, joined their family circle and gave more cause to delay their big adventure.

How many times in the generations of the Yeoman family that descended from old John, the Puritan, had a young man paused to take account of the risk and prospects that went with settling on new land on a new frontier, one can only guess. Many hesitated, no doubt, until their lives were rooted in the communities where they were born, and their dream of fine houses surrounded by broad, fertile fields stocked with good herds—all growing out of the courage to go through the woods, over the hills, across the rivers, through the territories of hostile Indian tribes—became forgotten amid the monotony of labors in familiar surroundings. But others not only dreamed but packed their wagons and took the trails westward. One cleared a field along the Mohawk . . . another set a cabin on a green hill in Ohio . . . some settled on a plain in Indiana . . . others stacked sod to make low huts on the Nebraska prairie. Wherever they went, these restless, venturesome kin of John and Patricia Yeoman—and all those immigrant peoples who came later to American shores—were bent on expanding the total worth of this, their own America. This worth was something they could well understand and appreciate. It was the creation of food and shelter and clothing. It was the security that prevails where land is brought to cultivation and communities can exist where people serve one another with all that range of knowledge man has accumulated to heal the sick, make and use a machine, keep order and justice in his society, guide his spiritual development, school his children . . . and respectfully bury his dead. It was improvement in the way of life for more and more people in more and more ways. This was the worth, the values, the rewards that the Yeomans and their kind attained as they opened the new land frontiers and created thereon the farms that gave us the blessings of an expanding agriculture.

In the seventeenth, the eighteenth and the nineteenth centuries, an enterprising American could find one of these new land frontiers, and if he had the guts, the skills and the luck to make a go of it, he could create his own resources of food and property . . . his own self-made good and wholesome standard of living, almost entirely the product of his personal achievements in agriculture.

But there was a limit to the new land frontiers.

Just in the nick of time, Abner and Margaret Yeoman decided they would postpone their lifetime dream no longer; they would find themselves a homestead in the great, undeveloped Pacific Northwest.

And that was what they did.

2.

IN THE SPRING OF 1880 pioneers were pouring into the Pacific Northwest—searching for homesteads in one of the last great areas where free, wild land could be claimed, settled and hopefully brought under cultivation. Some plodded slowly over the winding Oregon Trail that led westward and northward across prairies and mountains and through the rough, narrow valleys. Others came, as did Abner Yeoman, by steamship through Pacific waters from California to the wide mouth of the Columbia River, cruising smoothly upstream for a hundred miles to an inland harbor where the Willamette River met the majestic Columbia. Here, on both the east and west banks of the Willamette, the campsites and stock corrals of the overland travelers flanked stores and shops set close to the rough wharves where the steamers docked. The place was called Portland.

When Abner arrived, Portland was thriving on the dreams, the traffic and trade of settlers finding homes in a great area extending over a hundred miles out around this busy hub of civilization. There were lumbermen all the way from the Maine woods scouting for mill sites in the coastal forests north and south of the frontier town; cattlemen coming in from ranges east of the mountains to load supplies on their pack mules and ride away on their sleek, high-spirited mounts; settlers bustling around to fill their wagons with provisions and tools for their farms in the valleys to the south and west; husbands and fathers waiting at the docks to pick up their wives and children when steamers arrived. The board walks fronting the shops along the streets—always messy with mud or dust—were scarred by the hobnails in lumberjacks' boots and the spurs of swaggering cowhands, and scuffed delicately by the tread of Indian moccasins and the high laced shoes of pioneer dames. The stores sheltered jumbled heaps of clothing, foods and gear, and the odor of kerosene, leather and smoked salmon lay heavy on the shopper's nostrils.

Land agents in their small, boxlike offices squeezed in between saloons, inns and stores shuffled their maps and documents while they kept their customers spellbound with a constant palaver of soil depths, rainfall, climate and crops. The inns and boarding houses swarmed with engineers, surveyors, land speculators and drifters. Missionaries and fanatics came forward to save your soul—and gamblers, pimps and drunkards willingly suggested ways you could lose it. Ships from the Orient deposited stowaway Chinese, some to wash the soiled clothing of the endless stream of frontier travelers, and some to ride off with pack strings to become the cooks and flunkies for mines, ranches and logging camps.

Abner soon learned that most men in Portland had a horse to trade or a land of promise to brag about. It was easy to get yourself a no-good, spavined steed or a long, wearisome trip to a section where the available land offered the homesteader 160 acres of rock or sagebrush. After days of cautious inquiry, Abner put his faith in an agent who guided him eastward up the Columbia. Here he found prairie country, handicapped by scant rainfall, but blessed with soil that supported bunchgrass as high as a man's belt—soil that promised to surrender willingly to the plow.

His quest at an end, Abner filed his claim and joyfully posted a letter to Margaret telling her about his plans and the arrangements he would make to meet her and their children in Portland. Thus began the last venture of the Yeoman family to create agricultural prosperity on a wild new land frontier.

Let us keep in mind this picture of two frontiers—one an on-the-farm, earthbound agriculture advancing slowly across continents in the vanguard of civilization, and the other an off-the-farm archipelago of business linked to the land by farming's need for supplies and equipment or by farming's products that flow through its outposts where transportation, processing and merchandising put them in the hands of consumers. Let us remember that this pattern has been forming for a long, long time. We cannot say that in the year such-and-such we could walk to the clear-cut boundary of one frontier and step across a line into a new one, new in all respects, never penetrated, never explored. That is not the way frontiers wait for us.

Lewis and Clark made a remarkable expedition into North-

west Territory in 1804–6. They returned to assure young
America that a great new land area to the west did, indeed,
exist. But they were by no means the first white men to appreciate this remarkable fact. Long before their great adventure,
hunters, traders, trappers had scouted its potentials—had, in
fact, gone there to get furs and returned to sell them. And the
path taken by Lewis and Clark up rivers, across mountains and
down the wide Columbia to the Pacific did not cross the region
off the list of frontiers. For a hundred years and more, the area
continued to offer frontiers for farming, mining, lumbering.
The point is that a few penetrations, a few scouts back and
forth across a frontier's boundary do not mean that the
area is conditioned to man's use to the point that its status
has matured and the adventurer, the pioneer, the young hopeful may as well look elsewhere for a fresh, new, in-on-the-
ground-floor start on opportunity.

So it is with the agribusiness idea.

It's a new frontier because we are only now waking up to
the fact that it's there, that people have found it, that they've
gone into it and come out with more of the things men desire.
Some of this adventuring has spanned many centuries. Scouts
have penetrated the agribusiness frontier as unnoticed as the
anonymous trappers who took beaver pelts out of the Northwest's mountain-bordered valleys long before Lewis and Clark
gave the area an official inspection.

The first scouts to drift across our agribusiness frontier were
the traders . . . and after them came the inventors. These
amazing breeds of men have been to agribusiness what the
scouts in their coonskin caps have been to our continental
wilderness. Down through the centuries they have ridden
deep into territory where foundations for the agribusiness idea
were laid because they chanced to open the trails. Conse-

quently, while Abner Yeoman roamed among the shops and stores of the new city growing up on the end of the Oregon Trail, he was actually putting his destiny in the hands of these agribusiness scouts, the traders and the inventors.

What does a man need for a single-handed conquest of a wild piece of western prairie?

Well, first, he needs the means to carry family, equipment and provisions to their destination. For Abner, this could be only one thing—a wagon. To produce a wagon, however, required skills and tools and materials unfamiliar or unavailable to the man who farmed. Abner's answer was to buy a wagon.

Abner could count himself lucky that business enterprise had placed a variety of wagons in the shops that had sprung up along the Portland waterfront. He could consider the big, rugged wagons designed to carry great burdens of ore or lumber. Or he could buy a light rig called a hack, pulled by two horses, but lacking capacity for much of a load. But what Abner selected was a sturdy, middle-size wagon that a team could pull empty at a trot if speed was important, or that could be loaded with a ton of supplies or crops for slow hauling across primitive roads. This was the conventional home-steader's wagon, and it suited Abner very well.

Then he bought a moldboard plow—and when placed on its side, it fitted neatly under the wagon's seat. This was the type of plow that Thomas Jefferson improved in design and Jethro Wood developed for the cast-iron model he patented in 1814. Now this one Abner purchased was an excellent piece of equipment. Thanks to John Deere's improvements, it had a sharp steel point and a polished share. These features enabled it to slide through moist soil, turning over a neat, smooth roll of earth as fast as a team and teamster could walk.

Beside the plow, Abner stowed a bag of parts for a spike-tooth harrow—something an unknown inventor designed to be made by driving the spikes through planks of green oak bound together to make a grid six or eight feet square. And Abner bought a keg of square-head nails, a pick, spade, pitchfork, hoe, rake, scythe, ax and heavy cross-cut saw—items that agribusiness explorers long ago contrived to use in building a hardware trade that served farming country far and wide.

And to these items Abner added lamps and lanterns and kerosene to use in them . . . and silently gave his blessing to unknown inventors who figured out this way to brighten the nights in a far-off wilderness.

A barrel of flour, a barrel of salt pork, a bag of beans, another of coffee, a box of tea leaves, sacks of salt and sugar and cans of pepper and spices—these Abner placed in his wagon, mindful that he was fortunate they were available, but not realizing that they were treasures brought to man by the adventurous scouts of agribusiness who had crossed an earthbound frontier somewhere in the haze of history and begun a food traffic that was to grow as big as mankind's desires can make it.

Abner's wife, Margaret, was a good-looking woman. And when she led their two small children down the gangplank the day their boat docked in Portland's harbor, pioneer women who were watching took a good, long look at the clothes these newcomers wore. Margaret's skirt bulged wide and full from a slender, pinched-in waist. When she walked, its embroidered hem just skimmed above the ground. Her blouse was snug at the back and breast, but from the shoulders it puffed out in big, fancy sleeves that tapered into a snug fit along the forearm. Yards and yards of sturdy cotton cloth went into a dress like that. And yards more had been fashioned to make the washable garments worn by Mary and little Ben.

But cotton doesn't grow in the North Pacific country and the story of how cloth made of it came to be a matter of woman-to-woman comment on the docks of Portland, Oregon, more than seventy-five years ago only goes to show how winding can be the trails and how clever and resourceful the devices used by inventors and traders scouting the agribusiness frontier.

The cotton plant is not a native of North America, but travelers visiting colonies along the south Atlantic seaboard must have brought seed to this region—and there it became a popular flowering plant in the dooryard gardens of the colonists. Two hundred years ago it was inconceivable that cotton fabrics could become serious rivals of linens or woolens. To separate cotton fibers from the seeds to which they were attached required endless hours of tedious work to produce enough cloth for a dress. Once in 1739 a ship sailing out of Savannah took a bag of cotton to England . . . and eight bags coming from America in 1784 was such an astonishing quantity that British shippers and traders made a terrible fuss before they would believe that Americans could produce that much of the fluffy white stuff.

But that was the year that Edmund Cartwright invented the power loom and gave mankind a chance to shift from hand weaving to mechanical production of textiles. Then in 1793 Eli Whitney rigged up a machine that separated cotton from its seed. A man had to work two years to take the seed out of a bale (300 pounds was then the standard weight), but Whitney's gin, as the machine was called, could turn out almost that quantity of seed-free cotton in one day.

The year Whitney invented his gin, American cotton growers and traders were already thinking their progress was terrific because the cotton trading center at Charleston, South Carolina, had accumulated a million pounds to sell . . . but ten years later American sales to England rose to forty-one times that first million pounds.

So it was simple for Abner to dress his wife and children in pretty cotton dresses and to stow trunks laden with more cotton clothes in his homesteader's wagon. And along with the cottons were linens and woolens made easily available because Cartwright's power loom had spawned a great textile industry —one of the major outposts the inventor scouts had opened on the new frontier of agribusiness.

Abner and his family traveled more than a hundred miles by wagon to reach his homesteader's claim. It was situated forty miles from an army post, the nearest place to show the mark of a settled community. The prairie's rolling expanse of bunchgrass was dotted here and there by a settler's cabin, and the only road was an Indian trail. The Indians? Perhaps friendly; perhaps not.

Abner's first tasks were to build a log cabin and cut enough wild hay to winter his cow and horses. There was no brook or spring on Abner's homestead, so he hauled water from a stream two miles away. Soon after he was "settled," Abner learned that he could buy an adjoining homestead right—so, equipped with ax, spade, plow, cow and team of horses, he squared off to add 320 acres to Uncle Sam's count of useful land.

In the next twenty years, Abner split rails to fence his property—two and one half miles, allowing for fifty-fifty stretches between his and neighboring properties. He built a frame shack and a frame barn, leaving the original log cabin for a tool shelter. Then he started an eight-room, two-story house and finished it in two years. He teamed up with water-needy neighbors and together they bored the center out of pine logs to make seven miles of pipe to carry creek water to half a dozen ranches. He plowed down the bunchgrass and cut away the scattered pine trees to put approximately 250 acres in tillage—mostly devoted to wheat on an every-other-year cropping system with "summer fallow" cropless years between the plantings.

Fortunately, Cyrus Hall McCormick invented a reaping machine (in 1831), otherwise Abner might as well have left his new plow and harrow in Portland and contented himself with life as a hunter and herder on the broad prairie. For without the reaping machine it would have been folly to plant more grain than a man could cut with a scythe or cradle during the brief period the crop stands ripe before the kernels shatter out of the heads and are wasted on the rough surface of the field. The homesteader with a big family of husky sons might plant and harvest a worth-while acreage—but how about Abner with only a wife and two young children?

Up to the time when McCormick began making his reapers, the size of a field of wheat, oats or barley on any farm was limited by the capacity of the men available for hand-harvesting the crop. The sum of the crops for community, county, state and nation was the sum of all the scythe wielders' work, sunup to sundown, during the ripe grain season. Large areas of grain plantings were cut half ripe to make hay for horses and cattle. Another substantial portion of the crop was threshed on the farm, carted to the local grist mill for grinding, and taken back to the farm to feed the major part of the population which in those days was living and working on the land. Only a small portion of our pre-reaper grain crops flowed away from the farms to form the basis for agribusiness in the processing and merchandising of grain products.

On Abner's ranch, obtaining water became a serious problem. That pine-log pipe began to rot away a few years after it was installed and the neighbors bickered over who would fix each succeeding leak. Eventually Abner became so exasperated that he decided to avail himself of the new, "modern" service of well drilling. The drillers came and they struck water at 360 feet—and at a cost that wiped out years of Abner's savings. The only way to use the new deep well was to pump water by wind power. Abner figured out a way to do it. First he bought a huge steel tank that would hold 1,000 gallons. This he skidded into position on heavy-timbered stilts above the well. Then he needed a windmill, a mechanical contrivance weighing close to a ton. He planned to set the windmill with its twelve-foot diameter rotary on a tower forty feet above gound level. What sort of skyhooks were available to lift a ton of steel forty feet into the clear blue sky?

Abner and a fellow pioneer tackled this engineering feat as if it were as simple as your Saturday task of putting a new washer in a leaky water faucet. They built a supporting framework so that they could construct the windmill tower on its side with its lower "toes" touching the uprights of the pedestal that held the water tank. Then they assembled the windmill mechanism at the tip of the tower, taking advantage of high ground to avoid lifting the heavy machinery. The tower's construction was completed at an angle so that leverage with block and tackle anchored to a big tree and powered by a team of horses could lift the tower, windmill and all, into a vertical position. Imagine the anxiety when twenty feet of tower and a ton of windmill teetered into place atop a twenty-foot-high pedestal!

But this was only an ordinary sample of the way our pioneering ancestors used toil, ingenuity and their commonplace farm equipment to provide for their farms the counterpart that modern farmers employ as engineers and skilled labor or buy in the form of special machines—the services and supplies which today's farm income is called upon to provide in the agribusiness era.

Abner's main concern was to feed his family. One of his early projects was to start an orchard, and little by little it stretched away from the kitchen garden close to the house . . . stretched until it covered about ten acres! Growing and fruiting in Abner's orchard were at least a dozen varieties of apples, ranging from the early Yellow Transparent to the late hard-as-a-rock Russet. He grew half a dozen varieties of pears—early ones, pickle types, late ones. He set out an international assortment of prune trees—French, German, Italian. He added plums of half a dozen varieties. Cherries? He grew sour, pie varieties; blond, sweet kinds; dark, rich brunets that were big and sweet. Then he added quinces, apricots, walnuts and crab apples. South of the trees, he built grape trellises for five kinds of grapes. Around the kitchen garden, he set out red and black currants, gooseberries, blackberries, raspberries and elderberries. Oh, yes, and peaches—some of the white, squishy kind too delicate to ship, but luscious beyond compare—and big yellow Elbertas that can so perfectly, and Hales that ripen late and blend into whipped cream and biscuit to make a heavenly shortcake.

All this—except the Italian prunes—was just to embellish Abner's own table. He did overdo the prune planting until he grudgingly recognized that selling prunes was better than seeing them go to waste. So he invented a wood-burning drier to condition his surplus Italian prunes for storage. And people

31

came from far away to see how he designed this contraption. Time and again Abner sat up late sketching plans of his drier to mail to farmers who inquired about his design. Wherever men developed successful devices for processing farm products, they were in a position to add something to the usefulness of those products. A product such as fruit, when processed, is thus converted to something more stable and valuable in the market place. Although he did not succeed in developing a significantly profitable dried-prune business, Abner was, indeed, exploring the kind of enterprise out of which great agribusiness developments materialize.

Abner kept a few cattle. One of these would be the family cow that provided plenty of milk and cream for the table. Sometimes he vealed a calf, but, not liking butcher chores, he usually traded his surplus beef stock for credit at the country store. But there was always pork, produced more or less as a by-product of the farm's harvested crops. Abner was a master at preparing sausage, scrapple and head cheese, and his ham and bacon were matchless in cure and taste. Never was there a shortage of fresh eggs—and many were the young, tender cockerels which crowed at Sunday sunrise and by early afternoon found themselves frying to feed a carriage load of after-church visitors who arrived unannounced.

Abner knew how to clean a bushel of his soft white winter wheat and crack it in an old coffee mill to make as agreeable a breakfast cereal as ever came from Battle Creek. And he had a method for concentrating the sweet juice of pears to make a sirup that turned a stack of wheat cakes into something better than *crêpes Suzette*. Nor must we forget the shelves and shelves of canned fruits, pickles, jams, jellies and preserves that Margaret and daughter Mary stockpiled every summer.

Such was the way Abner provided a good living for his family for a third of a century between 1880 and 1915. Think of it—barely more than forty years ago, Abner on his farm on a new, wild land frontier had nearly the same earthbound self-sufficient way of life as did his Puritan ancestors nearly 300 years ago. What Abner and his fellow pioneers did not know was that while this new land frontier was vanishing, a new kind of frontier was forming—one that existed in the businesses relating to farming, businesses which changed and expanded agriculture more and faster than did the breaking in of vast acreages of wilderness. Step by step, the development of this new frontier of agricultural businesses provided the framework for the concept of a unified agricultural and business economy—the idea of an agribusiness economy.

3.

Sir John Lawes established the first agricultural experiment station in England in 1843. This was at Rothamsted in Harpenden, and the men who went there to work with Sir John began a new kind of conquest we now call agricultural research . . . and what they began doing was destined to affect significantly the outlook of every man who made his living by farming. Researchers build the roads that carry an increasing traffic across the borders of the new frontier of agribusiness —roads that change the course of farming. Often they follow the trails blazed by the traders and inventors we have described as the scouts of this promising area of opportunity. Their milestones are improvements in methods and products. In fact, the first agricultural researchers applied their knowledge of science in concerted efforts to improve farm crops. At Rothamsted, for instance, studies were devoted principally to cereal grains, wheat and barley in particular. The original station was situated on Sir John's estate and for many years he conducted its work at his own expense, eventually creating a trust to continue its operations indefinitely.

What Sir John and his associate Sir J. H. Gilbert initiated gradually awakened the interest of agricultural leaders all over the world. The Rothamsted station was in its fourteenth year when an American Congressman, Justin Morrill of Vermont, introduced a bill in Congress to establish, through the aid of public land grants, state colleges for the purpose of teaching agriculture and the mechanic arts. Morrill's bill had been vetoed by President Buchanan, but in 1862 President Lincoln signed it. Some years later a system of state agricultural experiment stations was linked to the development of the land-grant colleges. The country's first station, however, was established at Wesleyan University, Middletown, Connecticut, in 1875. Then followed the land-grant college stations at Ames, Iowa; Urbana, Illinois; Lincoln, Nebraska; Amherst, Massachusetts; State College, Pennsylvania; and Madison, Wisconsin.

All of this would have been dear to the heart of George Washington. These developments—although they occurred nearly a century too late to have assisted him in his progressive farming program at Mount Vernon—represented the application of brain power to explore possibilities, test theories, and compare methods, crops and breeds through accumulation of facts and observations much the way Washington himself undertook to do.

This much progress in the direction of agricultural research was promising, but it took the efforts of men such as Gregor Johann Mendel, the Austrian abbot, who studied the science of heredity and gave us Mendel's Law in 1865 to show the world the beginnings of the great progress that research could accomplish in agriculture. He was one of the great pioneers of research who blazed a trail into the wilderness of agricultural genetics which is yet to be followed to its end.

Five years before Abner became a pioneer settler in the Pacific Northwest, a young man named Luther Burbank established an experimental farm at Santa Rosa, California, and launched a career that focused people's attention on the amazing possibilities that lay ahead in agricultural experiments and research. Dust from broken stone had forced Burbank from his trade as a stone cutter in Massachusetts. To escape the same threat of tuberculosis that put Abner on his road to farming, Burbank turned to the occupation of truck gardening. While thus engaged, he dug the hill of potatoes that led mankind to see visions of new abundance, new quality and new wealth brought about by a magic touch as wonderful as a rub of Aladdin's lamp.

Why, Burbank asked, must a hill of potatoes turn out to be a vexing assortment of all sizes, shapes and colors? Wasn't there some way to select seed potatoes that would yield uniformly good tubers? Burbank worked four years to find an answer and when he found it he gave his name to a variety that amazed and pleased potato growers wherever it was planted.

This initial success fired young Burbank with bigger ideas. To apply them, he realized he needed to work in an area where climate, soil and growing conditions would make it possible to experiment with a wide range of plants. This led to his locating in central California. There he became the world-renowned "plant wizard." His productions poured out like Hollywood's pictures—and for the while they received publicity almost as sensational. Though many of his achievements, such as producing a fruit-bearing, spineless cactus, have washed out as far as significant economic importance goes, they did proclaim to the world that ideas, plus the hard work of research and experimentation, can produce the veritable two blades of grass where one grew before.

Nobody ever said it any better than Burbank himself: "One more grain to the head of wheat, rye, barley, oats or rice; one more kernel of corn to the ear; one more potato to the hill or peach, pear, plum, orange or nut to the tree would add millions of bushels to the world's supply, millions of dollars to the world's wealth, not for one year only but as a permanent legacy."

Abner Yeoman kept his eyes open for every new report of Burbank's achievements . . . and, like countless other men seeking a better living from their land, he put cash on the barrelhead for nursery stock that promised to bring a bit of the wizardry of the great plant breeder to his own homestead. One of Burbank's most significant projects was his work with plum varieties. He developed about sixty of these, and some of them —more commonly known as prunes—were used extensively in developing the tremendous dried-fruit enterprise that spread to farms throughout much of the Pacific Coast region. Abner's orchard demonstrated some of the possibilities in this enterprise, and there were years when he collected a tidy cash income from the output of his own small drying unit.

When the Department of Agriculture was established in the sixties, a young Scotchman named William Saunders was appointed superintendent of its new experimental gardens, and thus began the career of another researcher who added much to the highway system leading deep into the frontier of agribusiness. Saunders, like Burbank, was both green-thumb artist and plant-variety adventurer. He promptly set out thousands of shrubs and plants ranging from such common crops as wheat and clover to rare, unusual plants from far-off Brazil and Australia. He tried lucerne grass—later called alfalfa—and concluded that its nodular roots didn't matter—in fact, although he didn't know the bumps on its roots were made by nitrogen-storing bacteria, he did know that alfalfa made good forage, and crops of grain that followed it produced bigger yields. Abner, alert to these exploratory projects, secured some alfalfa seed and planted it next to the orchard where the family milk cow could be handily pastured. When, one morning, the dew was slow to evaporate from the trefoil leaves of his alfalfa plants, Abner's cow bloated and died. He knew then that there was cause for caution in using strange new crops, however promising they might appear to be.

But if Abner Yeoman had selected the right part of California and settled there instead of pioneering in the Pacific Northwest, this man Saunders might have been instrumental in making Abner's farming prospects fabulously better than they were. Ten years before Abner set out to find his homestead, Luther C. Tibbetts moved from Maine to a dry spot in southern California known as Riverside. He ditched water to his dusty 160 acres and set out fruit trees and grapes . . . and because he had faith in the work of Saunders and his associates, he seeded part of his land to alfalfa. Quite apart from his faith in alfalfa, however, Tibbetts had the luck to receive through a friend three graftings of a seedless orange tree that the Department of Agriculture imported from Brazil. Saunders called this particular tree the "Washington Navel" orange.

When Tibbetts' graftings bore fruit the blossom end of the orange had a puckered depression that looked just like something else—a navel. Growers were quick to notice, too, that these oranges were not only unique but also superior. They had

39

a rich, bright color; were big, seedless, juicy and delicious. Pretty soon there was a scramble to buy shoots from the Tibbetts trees. First the price for a single shoot was $10 . . . then $20 . . . then $100. Abner and Margaret Yeoman might have been among the fortunate who converted a seed orange grove to the seedless "Washingtons" in time to have reaped a fortune from the sale of cuttings, for the scramble to get the navel variety went on in earnest until 90,000 acres were planted to 720,000 trees—all descended from the three Tibbetts sprouts.

Of all the tasks and chores on the Yeoman homestead the one that young Ben liked the least was milking the family cow, and this dislike for the basic dairy operation was perhaps reason enough for him to be completely oblivious to the upsurge of another pattern of agricultural wealth even more fabulous than California's oranges. Hard on the heels of the researchers, who were testing metals and experimenting with alloys that would make the gears and driveshafts of the grain growers' machines more satisfactory, other researchers were busily developing applications of science that made the milk cow a mother lode of agricultural wealth.

More than twenty years before Abner settled on his homestead, Gail Borden had figured out a way to process cow's milk so that it could be sealed in a tin can and hauled to mining towns and loggers' camps for use many a mile and many a week away from the warm teats of the cow that gave it. Borden, a New Yorker, had roughed it across the frontiers of Texas and he knew well enough how death stalks through the wilderness in quest of the family that gets separated too far and too long from a storable supply of food. He worked a long time to produce a biscuit of corn meal and dried meat that would survive months of travel, sometimes over trails soaked with rain day-on-day, sometimes across scorching stretches of desert sands. He learned the strengths and weaknesses of the many molds and rots that spoil food, and by patient trials and tests he devised a recipe that withstood their attacks. Though Borden's biscuit tasted, so a cavalry officer said, like you know what, it would at least give a desperate human being the necessary nourishment to carry on until better fare was available. The army was wisely interested in the biscuit's possibilities as an emergency ration for troops on far-flung missions, but Borden's negotiations were somehow scuttled and his biscuit business floundered into bankruptcy.

His next idea was to concentrate and preserve milk so that its life-sustaining qualities could follow mankind safely and literally to the ends of the earth. Aided by a Shaker colony in eastern New York, he found that the vacuum boilers used in evaporating sap to make maple sugar were adaptable to reducing the water content of whole milk—and the thickened, yellowish fluid resulting from the process could be sealed in tin cans, transported easily and stored for use months after the milk had come from the cows. This time Borden's enterprise was successful—so successful, in fact, that it sent the fresh-milk merchants searching for ways to compete with the safe, clean, consistent product Borden had developed. Research put them on the trail of a preservative, too, and the one they selected was simple enough—cold temperature. They iced their shipments, cleaned up the worst of the filth that soured their product, and kept the "canned cow" from dominating the dairy markets.

Two other men of science came forward with ideas that helped the dairy cow compound a contribution to agricultural wealth during the years when Abner was taming a half-section of wild prairie in the northwest corner of the country, and his son Ben was learning the whims and frailties of the ever-increasing assortment of farm equipment.

41

One of these was the great Frenchman Louis Pasteur, who discovered bacteria. These creatures, Pasteur observed, could do great harm to things mankind needed or cherished. The big challenge was to stop them before they could do their damage. Pasteur reasoned that, as with larger living things, death would come to bacteria if they were subjected to a temperature higher than they could take. While one could not use heat to kill bacteria in the blood stream without injuring and perhaps killing the host, bacteria in an inanimate substance could surely be tortured to death if their environment was made hot enough. So it was that his experiments led to heating milk to arrest bacterial action. He found that by controlling the temperature carefully and timing the duration of the heating period just right, the taste of the milk would not be impaired and enough of the bacteria could be killed so that it would not turn sour or spoil for hours or even days longer than raw milk would stay sweet. His method became known as pasteurizing . . . and its use, plus cooling practices, made it possible for distant dairy herds to supply fresh fluid milk for city consumers.

The other scientist was an American—Stephen Moulton Babcock. In 1890 he perfected a method for measuring the percentage of butterfat in milk, a simple combination of chemistry and physics that became known as the Babcock test. This was an important landmark in the dairy business because it established an accurate means of valuing milk and cream in relation to the way these products might be used. Cows, individually and by breeds, vary in the cream or butterfat content of their milk. In other words, some cows' milk will yield more butter than will others'. Some of the early-day milk suppliers were accused of considering it a matter of clever business tactics to add water to their milk, but the Babcock test was capable of spotting this trick because it would reveal that the adulterated milk had a butterfat content lower than any respectable cow would yield. Of greater merit, however, was the application of the test in grading milk or cream according to its fat content so that the distributor and manufacturer could standardize their operations, and also so that the milk producer could reckon the value of his product in relation to the markets for butter, cheese and fresh fluid milk.

Over the road of Babcock's research in milk testing marched an ever-growing cavalcade of dairy farming and dairy marketing developments. His test became the basis whereby cattle breeders measured and compared the producing ability of dairy breeds and the cow families within these breeds. Linked to this came the proved sire program, the means to identify the bulls that, through the science of genetics, could be used to improve the milk-producing capacity of every dairy herd in America. The Babcock test provided basic qualifications for the milk that poured into manufacturing plants to become cheese or ice cream, dry milk powder or evaporated milk. It gave the dairy farmers of southern Wisconsin or northern Vermont who skimmed their milk with separators and sold only the cream a means of understanding their relationship to the country's butter markets. And because of Babcock's test, the housewife could be confident that the bottle of milk left on her doorstep tomorrow would be the same in cream (butterfat) content as yesterday's.

Long after Abner had won his battle for an assured abundance of food from his land, this researcher, Babcock, discovered that nourishment from what we eat comes partly from something more elusive than the visible, measurable substances heretofore known to us. In his Wisconsin laboratory, he set to work on some feeding experiments to check on his doubts that the conventional analysis of food and the energy content theory were satisfactory indexes of the nutritional value of diets. The result was that he helped to discover the existence of a nutrient factor we now call vitamins. Right away, the road builders of agribusiness, the researchers, began paving new highways and constructing new bridges destined to carry us far into another part of the new frontier of agribusiness. Every food we eat, every eatable product from the farm, has been reappraised in terms of vitamins . . . and the businesses in processing, preserving, balancing and supplementing vitamin qualities in foods and feeds are becoming as multiple as the cuttings from Luther Tibbetts' navel orange trees.

But this is getting far ahead of our story. Abner Yeoman never heard of a vitamin in all his long life . . . though he did, no doubt, consume more of them every day from his own wholesome food resources than many a city dweller eats nowadays even though they are sold in concentrated, measured and identified units in every corner drugstore. Abner was a man who took pride in being a good provider, and for him the way to be one was to grow a great abundance and variety of good things to eat. Years later, the researchers found proof that Abner had a good idea.

But if Abner's quest for a great variety of foods had extended far enough, he might have added the soybean to his garden plants, never dreaming that in the sundown of his lifetime the researchers would put this round little bean to more uses than he could name for all the fruits and roots, the nuts and kernels, the stalks and leaves of all the plants he grew. For centuries, the soybean has provided wholesome food for man and his domestic livestock in the Orient. Some adventurer brought seed to America in 1804, and for decades thereafter it was grown in botanical gardens as a curiosity. Years before

Abner was born, a Japanese agriculturist lecturing in New York told about its varied uses . . . some varieties producing a table vegetable like peas, some a leafy hay crop, others grown for grain which could be ground to produce a rich and wholesome feed meal. That this meal was oil-bearing was scarcely noticed in America until 1915.

Then the researchers and traders became interested.

Whereas Abner and his family might have tried soybeans from the farm's big garden and rated them as much less tasty than the spotted or brown or lima beans familiar in most homesteaders' kitchens, the researchers of a later day ground the hard, ripe beans, heated the resulting meal and applied pressure to squeeze out a remarkable proportion of oil. The meal, minus the oil, made a valuable livestock feed, a base for a new and better glue, a casein useful in paint or for paper sizing, and a protein that could be transformed into plastics for a thousand purposes. And the soybean oil—the researchers refined it and processed it to make salad oil, shortening, a butter substitute, paint, printing ink and soap, to mention just a little of its versatility.

Abner and Margaret Yeoman considered lard from the hogs grown and butchered on the farm quite adequate for shortening and for making a good lye soap that would wrench the dirt out of a farmer's grimy overalls. And to bother about a substitute for the sweet, golden butter made from a good cow's cream was unthinkable.

The new areas of agribusiness thrown open by the inventors, the traders and the researchers attracted ambitious, resourceful settlers—the businessmen. Although they didn't know it, they were *agribusinessmen*. They were men with ideas, and often they used their ideas very successfully in making money. The businessmen, for instance, began to see the opportunities to profit from the new products and new methods the researchers developed.

Businessmen by the name of Swift, Armour, Wilson and Cudahy had magnified the butcher's services into an extensive operation now called "packing." Great stockyards sprawled on the fringes of Chicago, Kansas City, Cincinnati and St. Louis. Close by stood the huge slaughterhouses, in and out of which moved hundreds of carloads of cattle, hogs and sheep every working day. In the beginning of the packing industry, meat was salted or pickled in preparation for distant markets. To provide fresh meat for cities far from the livestock belt animals were shipped alive over the rails, the canals and the rivers and distributed to local butchers. But the researchers were busy and in the early seventies they had some improvements ready. First, they developed chilling processes. They designed refrigerated freight cars, thus making it possible to ship fresh meat longer distances. This greatly extended the markets for the packing plants in the stock feeding areas and intensified the concentration of packing operations in these livestock marketing centers. With this concentration came two more challenges to the researchers.

One was the upsurge of livestock diseases, which became alarming—and often disastrous—as a consequence of the movement of great numbers of animals to concentration centers for feeding, trading and shipping. The public, too, developed an uneasiness over whether its pot roasts, bacon slabs and mutton chops were from slaughtered stock, or sick animals that expired too soon to walk up the ramps to the killing floors. Concern about these problems led to establishment of the Department of Agriculture's Bureau of Animal Industry and laws to set up federal meat inspection in the packing plants. Texas fever, a disease transmitted by a tick in the warmer climates, was brought to bay by the researchers who learned how to destroy ticks by dipping cattle in vats filled with a solution fatal to the pests. As soon as one dangerous infestation of parasites or epidemic of a contagious disease could be checked, another would threaten . . . so the researchers were busy with a never-ending quest for medicines, pesticides, vaccines that would keep livestock alive and healthy.

The other big challenge to the researchers resulting from the enormous concentrations of meat-packing operations dealt with uses for animal by-products. Abner and his fellow homesteaders, butchering their own hogs, could be thrifty or extravagant as they pleased about the way they used blood (for blood pudding, for instance) and brains (to feed the family cat or dog) and intestines (for sausage casings or for burying beside a berry bush for fertilizer)—but all these oddities had been freighted into the packing houses and had to be freighted out again either as waste or for some useful purpose. So the researchers had mountains of guts and blood and slippery trimmings to think about. Little by little, their ingenuity transformed the piles of gore into valuable products until, as is commonly said, a use has been found for everything but the squeal of a hog. Glands provided extracts, insulin for example, that prolonged human life and health. Blood and bone and scraps became supplemental feeds bolstering the health of livestock. Offal and waste became dry, powdered fertilizer. Hair and bristles and skins found multiple uses in industry. And after the roasts and chops, the bacons and hams, had all been trimmed and readied for sale, the scraps were transformed into tasty hashed, minced, casing-covered or canned products of endless variety . . . and America's devotion to the hot dog became monstrous, indeed.

47

YOUNG BEN YEOMAN was only vaguely aware that the researchers were tinkering with the homestead's crop that interested him more than all the others—the broad acres of winter wheat. He remembered that hot July day, years before, when he discovered that the headed wheat at the border of Abner's big field, some twenty acres at the time, would just reach to his chin . . . and how he had ventured cautiously, step by step, into the expanse of green-yellow grain, wondering if any of it was tall enough to tickle his nose. And just before he reached what seemed to be the tallest portion, his sister Mary shrieked, "Get out of there! You'll tramp down bushels and bushels. You'll catch it!"

This was in the period when Abner scattered his seed wheat

by hand; "broadcast," the method was called. The grains sprouted helter-skelter and there were no drill rows for little Ben to follow. Sometimes Abner's casts overlapped and too many kernels sprouted in a small area, each producing a frustrated crown from which "stooled" a cluster of spindly straws —and the whole overplanted spot grew up to grasslike stalks with puny heads. But where kernels fell well spaced a strong crown as big as Ben's fist "stooled" out vigorously with a cluster of sturdy straws atop of which drooped the handsome heads, longer than a boy's finger and bulging with off-set rows of fat kernels.

For ten, twelve, almost fifteen years, Ben watched his father struggle against the great spread of wild prairie and the scattered groves of pine and oak that jutted into the lengthening furrowed strips. Often he trudged the two miles across the prairie from the one-room shack called the district school and loaded surface rocks on an empty stone sledge before coming to the house for a cup of milk and a handful of his mother's oatmeal cookies. Then after gulping his refreshments, he would harness the team and draw the sledge to a rock pile, unload it and race the dumpy pair of draft mares back to the barnyard minutes before dusk and seconds ahead of the call to supper. But it was diligence like this that enabled Abner and Ben to plow under the bunchgrass on a few more acres every spring until all the good land in Abner's half-section was ready for cropping. Ben was nearly twenty when the last strip of virgin sod was put to plow ... and after that it seemed there never was time for additional conquest even if more bunchgrass prairie had been available. Now it was a race against the calendar to plow and harrow, work the summer fallow and seed the fall planting, cut and gather the hay and harvest the crop. The farm's 250 cultivated acres, half of it bearing wheat every year, was enough.

Beginning with the turn of the century, old Abner was vaguely aware that his prosperity was a mixture of providing a luxurious variety of food from his barnyard, orchard and garden and of cash received for the wheat he grew and sold. At first, the dollars he added to his bank deposits each year, sometime between harvest and the day he chose to sell his crop, seemed like Cinderella's adventure with the prince . . . a turn of fortune far beyond his fondest dreams. There were sobering experiences later, however. The threshers' bill cut deep into the income. And there were grain sacks to buy, and wire to replace the decaying rail fences, and harness and nails and sometimes a new variety of seed wheat. As the months passed, the money from the year's crop melted slowly away like a drift of snow, resisting the warm breath of spring for a while and then trickling away until all was gone.

The new wheat varieties were alternately a plague and a blessing in the life of young Ben. Sometimes the chosen newcomer grew tall—and this made it necessary to handle many tons of long, awkward straw to harvest the immature wheat cut around the borders of the fields to make hay for the farm's horses. On the other hand, Abner's venture with the hard-seeded Turkish wheats, much desired by the flour millers, resulted in vexations with straw too short to lift the heads high enough so the reaper's sickle bar could snip them without gouging into the hard-baked earth of the fields. Cutting the short varieties involved time-wasting maneuvers as well as numerous breakdowns because the reaper's sickle had to be set so low it was menaced by stumps and stones that could be avoided in taller wheat. Sometimes a new variety gave great promise for one or two seasons, then smut would ravage the next crop, or a sudden spell of hot winds would shatter the grain heads if they were not the kind that resisted the overripening effect of a scorching fortnight.

None of these difficulties, however, were particularly discouraging to the Yeomans and their fellow wheat growers. From the time Abner cut his first, small wheat crop and right on until years after young Ben was a grown man and responsible for most of the farm's operations, the wheat producers of America were almost constantly putting more acres in this cereal crop, harvesting greater quantities, finding export trade that consumed a hundred and sometimes two hundred million bushels a year, and enjoying the way the country's city dwellers took to the fad of eating the white bread that used more bushels to fill a family's breadbasket than did the dark, whole cereal flours of an earlier day.

And while the researchers were busy with all the factors that might make more progress in wheat culture and use, a smart miller in Minneapolis, C. A. Pillsbury, hit on an idea that launched a great new segment of agribusiness. Only about 70 per cent of a kernel of wheat found its way into the sacks of refined white flour—and for a long time the rest, the dark and oily portions of a wheat kernel, was dumped into the rivers that flowed beside the flour mills. Pillsbury tried feeding these dark "shorts" and "middlings" to steers and discovered the resulting gains and finish were comparable to those produced by a generous ration of corn. He promptly closed the chutes in his mill where tons of the brown meals had plummeted into the Mississippi every day and henceforth sacked these mill products to sell as livestock feed. Very soon, Pillsbury's idea put the researchers on a new trail, and businesses devoted to the manufacture and distribution of mixed feeds for poultry and livestock crowded into positions along this new highway of opportunity that led out of the nation's wheat bins.

Old Abner Yeoman reached his threescore years and ten. Now there were young and spunky horses carrying the harnesses the elder Yeoman had buckled about the necks and bellies of his aging teams day on day, year on year. When Ben sputtered admonitions to be careful in harnessing or driving these frisky colts, the old man flinched a little—not from fear of the snorty young animals but from acceptance of the fact that a man, like an old horse, must someday settle to a slower pace and a lighter load. More fearsome to Abner were the machines. These did not slow down with age. They broke down. Their maintenance and repair was not a matter of rest or discreet limits to exertion like an old man would use to restore his fitness for another day's work. Their mending called for muscle enough to lift and skid a heavy bull wheel into position, or the deft, quick fingers that could set a tricky spring in place when a cam turned a jumble of confusing wheels and gears. Ben's younger, husky muscles and quick reflexes could meet these challenges. Finding it hard to adjust himself to machine operations, Abner fidgeted uneasily while Ben tinkered and strained to set up the newly uncrated pieces of equipment. Then a few years later, Abner's contact with the new machines was reduced to hovering silently near by, watching respectfully, and sometimes anticipating Ben's need for another wrench, larger or smaller. But merely being a wrench-hander was dull . . . and besides, a machine was a sterile, unlovely thing not at all as friendly and responsive as a vine or a bush or a tree. Old Abner quietly forsook the machine shed, picked up his well-worn hoe and honed a good, sharp edge on it with his peddle-powered grindstone; then he trudged off to hack the weeds that were trespassing in his kitchen garden.

Ben's life was spread down the drill rows of the newly seeded wheat every fall. He raced his span of heavy Percherons against the weather's fickle promise of an early rainfall, drilling, drilling, drilling, until a hundred and twenty acres were corduroyed by the seeder. Then he chored and fixed and patched and repaired the gear and buildings and machines while the rains came and the new grain sprouted, turned the fields into soft, lovely carpets richly green, which then disappeared under the white cloak of the winter's first snowfall. Come spring, Ben padded himself with long-john underwear, woolen shirts and heavy mackinaw to ride the slow-moving gang plow against the frosty prairie winds. Every spring, the same long exile amidst a black upheaval of crumbling earth . . . mile on mile, week on week. And then the dry days with the sixteen-foot harrow gliding ahead of him and the dust rising in a smothering fog, grimy, dirty, irritating torture. Next, the scurry to cut the big acreage of hay to feed the farm's six hefty teams. Now the sweet, rich odor of the sap flicked out of the cut stems of the young wheat; and after that the long, hot walk around the field setting up the bundles of bound grain to form the cocks for the week-long cure; the nights disturbed with scratching the vicious itch of the "fire weed" that adulterated the crop; and the sweaty days of dogged labor hoisting bundles from field to wagon, wagon to loft window, loft window to far corners of the hay mow. Finally, the recruiting of the small army of harvesters and the well-organized plunder of the golden acres of grain.

Abner's and Ben's experiences as grain farmers give us a picture of what happened in the span of fifty years. As fast as the pioneers expanded their cropland beyond the acreages they could harvest with their scythes, they would team up and buy one of the horse-drawn reaping machines.

Not only did this step toward mechanizing the farm produce great changes in farming operations, but it also marked a transition in the primary tasks and skills of the farmer. Abner, the pioneer, was primarily concerned with creating a productive establishment. He was a builder of house, barn, sheds and fences. He was a man with a green thumb who transformed the idle wilderness to a useful, fruitful expanse of grain fields, orchards and gardens. He was a herdsman who spared no effort to see that the newborn calf survived . . . that the lame horse was restored to sound condition . . . that every bird and beast was watered, fed and sheltered according to its need. Most of Abner's tasks and interests were applied to things he himself could create and conserve. But when machinery became a major factor in farm operations, it was the younger generation that gave it primary attention. Young Ben it was who uncrated the machine parts and studied the assembly diagrams, handled the wrenches and tinkered with the adjustments. Abner merely stood by and watched, muttering sometimes that the grain didn't run the right way to give the greatest strength to a wooden part, or that the bright red paint on a casting was hiding a flaw no conscientious foundryman should have allowed to leave the plant. Always the elements of creation were foremost in his concern.

But Ben, of the younger generation, was of a different mind. Would the bright, new assortment of metal and wood fit together like the plans said? Would the machine do its work? Would it really take some of the drudgery out of a farmer's tasks? What happened if one tightened the tension here; or slackened it there? A thousand questions came to mind as the enthusiastic young man sought to coax satisfactory performance from the gears and belts, the shafts and levers of the rattling, clumsy machines. With oil can, grease bucket and wrench, Ben hovered over these reluctant contraptions—and his tasks and skills dealt more and more with mechanical operations and repairs, constant repairs. Even the repairs about the farm were drifting away from Abner's self-sufficient creative skills. Time was when a broken section of fence was repaired by fresh-cut, new rails or boards custom-sawed from the farm's own timber. But more and more as Ben became the chief of operations, it was purchased barbed wire that repaired the fences. And the bills from the hardware and implement dealers grew bigger and bigger for oils, greases, metal parts and tools such as wrenches and soldering irons.

For Ben, these were mere signs along a trail leading to new adventure. When Abner allowed that the time had come for the farm to have its own private reaper, young Ben joined, in spirit, the proud fraternity of mechanized adventurers who were among the first to try the throttle of a locomotive, the wheel of a racing car, or—in our time—the controls of a jet plane. And so it was, with Abner and Ben having a reaper for their own private convenience, the new era of mechanized farming had begun on the Yeoman homestead.

The first of their reapers was a clumsy contraption that could cut a five-foot swath. It had four rakelike arms that dipped into the grain standing ahead of the sickle bar. These arms pushed the stalks against the cutting knives, and the cut grain was deposited on a wooden platform behind the sickle. When a big armful of grain had accumulated on the platform, the operator tripped a lever and the rakelike arm swept the grain off the platform. Two or three men with pitchforks followed the machine and piled several of these deposits into small stacks which were left in the field to dry thoroughly before they were hauled to the barnyard to be threshed. The first mechanical threshers were powered by horses—horses walking round and round pulling a pole that turned a set of gears which transmitted power to the machine that separated kernels from straw and chaff. All the able men in the community worked together to make up the harvest crews that moved from farm to farm until everybody's crop was cut, taken from the fields and threshed.

Soon better machines began to appear. One of these was the binder that replaced the reaper. This machine had clever mechanical fingers that tied a cord around an armful of grain, then dumped it where the operator wanted to place it. This made harvest work easier because the bundles of grain were much less difficult to handle than were the loose little heaps dumped behind a reaper.

Then came the big steam engine to replace the clumsy horse-powered machine that ran the threshers. The separator, too, was now designed to receive bundles as fast as men could toss them into its ravenous mouth. Enterprising men, privately or in small companies, bought the new threshing equipment and made a profitable business serving the grain producers.

Then the binder gave way to the header—a bigger machine that could cut a swath more than twice the width of a binder's sickle. Using a header required an integrated operation involving many men, machines and horses. One man, driving eight horses, piloted the header. This machine moved ahead of the horses, biting a twelve-foot swath out of the field of standing grain. Behind the header's sickle, a canvas belt traveled up an inclined spout, dumping headed grain into a wagon driven alongside. This wagon's bed was a big, lopsided box, low on its right side where the spout rode against it, and twice as high on its left side. A rope net spread in the empty box received the grain as it poured from the header's spout. A man known as the "loader" packed the grain evenly in the box, forking it forward until the packed load pressed him against the back of the box. Then at the loader's signal the header stopped and he sat on the spout until the next box drove up to be loaded.

Grain was stacked in the center of a field. Each boxload of grain was deposited there . . . placed according to the wishes of a proud tyrant called a "stacker." Building neat, rain-turning stacks required skill, and the man with the know-how for it was usually as bellicose as a top sergeant. When a box driver brought his load to the stack, he would place it parallel to the snap pole, a piece of wood the length of the wagon bed and fitted with short ropes with snaps at their ends. The stacker hooked these snaps to rings in the box net where it draped over the low side of the wagon bed. The driver pulled the other side of the net from over the high side of the box, across the load, and connected it to the cable drawn by the snap team. The driver of this team was usually the oldest or the youngest member of the crew. At the stacker's signal, the snap team driver whipped his sleepy horses into action and the ton or so of grain was quickly rolled into place on the stack. The completed stacks waited in the field until visited by the steam-powered threshing outfit on its circuit of dozens of farms in the community.

Counting header pilot, loader, stacker, snap driver and four box drivers, a header crew required eight men and eighteen horses. But this cumbersome combination of men, horses and equipment gave the grain farmer the means to increase his productive capacity very considerably . . . and it was the sum of these increases that made America capable of helping to feed its Allies during World War I.

The progress in improving planters, cultivators and harvesters was building agribusiness in two directions off the farm. It was creating a tremendous industry in the manufacture and distribution of farm machines; and it was multiplying the quanties of grain and grain-fed livestock that flowed away from the farms to seek consumption in agribusiness ventures operating far from the land that grew these products.

Came the year 1914. Ben's wheat sprouted smartly after a generous, blessed series of fall rains. Snow fell and spread a comforting white blanket over the tender green blades. War raged in Europe and wheat exports increased briskly. Wheat prices climbed to $1.40 a bushel. Showers pelted down on the wheat acreage of Abner and Ben Yeoman . . . and it was as if the sky were dripping silver coins. Their wheat grew shoulder-high, and the harvest poured out twice the yield they'd ever threshed. So did the crops on countless other farms—farms with nearly seven million new acres planted to wheat. Exports soared to a golden tide of fifty-five million dollars a month. But this was only nibbling at THE BIG CROP—a record harvest of more than a billion bushels. The market shuddered, then tumbled until it was back to prewar levels. Warily Abner and Ben watched THE BIG PRICE slip away . . . and finally sold their BIG CROP far short of the high mark.

DURING THE FORTY YEARS between 1880 and 1920, Abner Yeoman and his family lived close to a way of life that had prevailed almost unchanged since the days of the Puritans. Mostly it was a good way of life. It gave America the kind of people who had the strength of spirit to overcome the hardships confronting the pioneer without themselves becoming the human counterpart of the rough, unfriendly wilderness. Slowly, patiently, their labors lifted them from the crude cabins, huts and shacks to the farmsteads graced by spacious houses and orderly arrays of barns and sheds. Jacks-of-all-trades, they logged and cleared, and fenced and leveled, and stocked and seeded, and watered and drained, until pastures and crops spread endlessly across the landscape. They mingled at crossroads and villages and over their line fences, creating a society generally considered to be classless, respectable, friendly and wholesome.

This was the period that underscored the importance of the *family farm*—a widely accepted, though vaguely defined, image of a farming unit glorified to the point of becoming an institution in our array of social, economic and political factors. Farm leaders stressed that its prosperity was fundamental to the prosperity of the nation. Politicians said the family farm was the foundation of American democracy . . . social planners saw it as the core of the stable, well-balanced community . . . and the public at large presumed that it was a bulwark protecting an excitable electorate from radicalism, a sanctuary for the cherished expression of rugged individualism, a place where peace-loving, tranquil people lived by a code of plain common sense, a storm cellar in which a large part of the population could seek shelter whenever the economy was ravaged by depression.

Actually, the period between 1880 and 1920 was preceded by and included events, trends in farming and behavior by farming people that were to have far-reaching impact on the family farm in later years.

While the individual family such as Abner Yeoman's settled the wild, new land in humble gratitude for the opportunity to create an almost self-sufficient way of life on a new farm, the nation's land program as a whole was a vast patchwork of policies designed to get land settled as rapidly as possible.

The big surge of western settlement resulted from the passage of the Homestead Act in 1862. This act specified grants of 160 acres as a farming unit, a concept based on the soil, climate and rainfall characteristics of the area east of the Mississippi. But by the time the act was passed, the frontier for settlement had moved westward into the dry territory of the Great Plains, where most of the land called for more extensive forms of crop and livestock operations than those adaptable to the East. Hence in much of this area the 160-acre homestead was generally too small to be a satisfactory-sized unit for efficient operation.

Regardless of the enormity of the stage for the drama of earthbound agriculture, the setting for most of the scenes was, nevertheless, the modest farm where a family looked to the resources within its line fences to provide the essentials for its livelihood. Great as were the developments and the tensions of the period, their influence on the way of life of a farm family was tempered and obscured by lesser things, close at hand, that determined what would happen to this farm or that farm.

Abner Yeoman was the kind of farmer who left his bed at sunrise, and there were hours of choring and not a little hard work behind him when he came to the kitchen and changed to a clean jacket. Margaret was the zealous kind of home-maker who cooked a hearty breakfast, skimmed cream off the set pans that held the evening's milk, and pumped the dasher of the butter churn until her family gathered at the breakfast table.

Abner bowed his head for the mealtime blessing, and after breakfast the family went to the sitting room, where he read them passages from the Scriptures and led them in morning prayer. When they were young, Mary and Ben, slate and book in one hand, lunch box in the other, had hurried down the lane and cut across the fields on the two-mile hike to the district school. Abner put on his carpenter's apron and hastened away to his lumber pile. Margaret tidied up her kitchen, finished the churning and molded her butter, then settled to her stint of washing and mending clothes, hooking rugs or canning fruit.

Schooling a child much beyond the three R's was an unusual undertaking in a pioneer family, but when Mary finished her grades in the district school, Abner and Margaret arranged to send her to the proud little academy and college in Portland, and sooner than a young colt can grow to harness age she was back and ready to teach in one of the county's one-room schools. Custom was for the district's teacher to board at a good, respectable farm home . . . and quite often such homes had a bachelor son wondering where to find a wife. This, precisely, was the turn of events that led to Mary's wedding . . . and the slaughter of a goodly number of Abner's young roosters to fry in the farm's fresh, sweet lard and come brown and tender to the tables where friends and neighbors by the dozen gathered for Mary's wedding breakfast.

Margaret busied herself for months, hooking a special set of rugs for the sitting room in Mary's new home. The pattern called for a prim black border which she made from the suit that was Abner's best when they lived in California, and the background color was the reddish blue-brown of a heather woolen Margaret's Scotch mother had brought from her native glen. The center figures were great red roses, and Margaret left these to be completed last of all.

"You make it harder, doing it that way," Abner observed.

"I know, Abner," she replied, "but I just can't make up my mind to parting with my red skirt and cape—it's such a good piece of material."

"Then why don't you just dye some other cloth instead?" her husband asked.

"I've thought of that, but it's so hard to get just the right, soft shade," Margaret lamented.

Well, many a pioneer homemaker never finished hooking the last rug she started . . . and so it was with Margaret. A sharp, sudden pain in her chest, a frantic relay of fast riders to summon the town's white-whiskered doctor to gallop his carriage team the bumpy, dusty seven miles to the Yeoman home . . . all too late.

After Margaret died, Abner asked Grandpa and Grandma Graham to move in and give a hand at keeping things about the home in proper condition until the Yeomans, father and son, could get adjusted to managing the house themselves. The Grahams weren't really grandparents to anybody. Pa Graham had been in the capacity of an old gray handyman about the county ever since he was about fifty when he came to the prairie in the early nineties. Ben remembered they called him Grandpa when he came to the Yeomans' place that first summer to help with the haying. He was a wiry little man who always schemed to get the softer jobs, but everybody forgave him for that because he was always giving himself a jibe about being a "poor, old, no-account grandpa." Grandma Graham was a pink-cheeked little wisp of a woman who wore clean blue gingham dresses a size too large. She was a kind, jolly, folksy little person . . . but a terribly poor cook.

Old Abner—weary of Mrs. Graham's constant chatter and fearful that he'd offend her with a slip of his tongue that might reveal his opinion of her cooking—fixed himself a den in the wing of the big house, where he slept and kept his papers, read his magazines and played the old Estey organ he and Margaret had freighted up from San Francisco. Mindful of courtesies such as keeping up a pretense that the Grahams were welcome visitors and not household servants although paid well for their services, Abner cleverly established for himself a routine about the house that salved his conscience on this point and also gave him escape to his private den. He'd peel the potatoes for the evening meal, masking the act with the pretense that

he wanted the peelings for his milk cow. Then he'd milk and
skim the morning's cream, wash all the dairy vessels and after
supper split and carry in the next day's stovewood. This ex-
cused changing from barn clothes to house clothes and again
back to barn clothes and finally to house clothes. Whether
Grandma Graham caught on or not, she never said, but Abner
figured that somewhere in the confusion of his clothes changing, she would lose track of him and not think he was running
away from her after-supper chatter.

Shortly before the beginning of the second wheat harvest
with Grandma Graham managing the Yeoman kitchen, the
old lady announced that she had invited a niece, Betty Graham,
to come from Seattle to spend a month visiting and helping
with the canning and the harvest crew's tremendous meals.

"She's right capable and well brought up," Grandma declared. "You couldn't hire better help for five dollars a week—
but she'll be glad to give me a hand for three dollars." Abner
looked at his son, a twinkle in his old eyes.

"Now you see, Ben, why it's smart for a farmer to marry
his cook and housekeeper instead of paying her wages."

Ben winced at the jest. His image of the young woman soon
to be placing the platters and serving dishes on the Yeoman
table was of a fat, shapeless maid who responded to every comment with a silly giggle. And she'd probably have crooked
teeth and stringy hair. The real Betty, however, was a greater
shock to Ben than anything he could imagine. She wasn't fat.
She was trim and pretty. Her hair wasn't stringy; it was thick
and red and tied neatly in a cluster of curls. She didn't giggle
and expose teeth that pointed this way and that way. Her smile
was warm and cordial and she talked with an easy, friendly
air as if she had belonged in this house all her life. In all his
twenty-nine years, Ben had never met the likes of this.

66

It turned out to be a wonderful summer.

They were putting the header away for its hibernation between harvests when Abner spoke about the subject that had been on his mind for a long time—an understanding as to Ben's share in the farm's ownership and income. "You'll be getting yourself a wife one of these days, Ben," the old man began, "and I think it's high time you had some property of your own. You'll owe it to your wife to handle your money matters without your pa's having his hand on the purse strings, too." It was something Ben had thought very little about. In his boyhood, yes, in his early manhood, too, the farm's income in cash had been too meager to provide wages regularly for Ben. Whenever he needed personal things, Abner's purse was always generously opened to buy them. In a way, everything about the farm was "his," Ben well knew. What Abner began to say now, however, surprised and overwhelmed the younger man. It was fair and it was generous. Best of all, it was practical.

Abner proposed to deed to Ben the 160 acres that had no buildings; thus all of the crops from its fields would provide Ben's independent income. Then he would rent the rest of the farm, the part with the house and barns, to Ben at the customary crop-sharing rentals. In return for his privilege of food and lodging, Abner would give Ben all of the farm's livestock and equipment, and thereafter Ben would buy with his own money whatever new machines or stock he might require. Then Abner spoke of the will he planned to make. He would leave to his daughter Mary the legacies he had received from the estates of his father and an uncle because he figured the value of these investments about matched the remainder of his homestead which he would leave to Ben.

"That way, the home will be all yours, Son, so you can count on it . . . and you may as well hustle around and get yourself a wife and fill some of those extra bedchambers with a flock of little Yeomans," Abner advised.

Betty left the Yeoman homestead just long enough to go back to her Seattle home and prepare for her wedding in late autumn. She and Ben journeyed by steamboat to Victoria, British Columbia, for their wedding trip . . . Ben wearing the high, stiff collars that tortured a man who spent his life in the great outdoors; Betty sparkling like a princess under a big hat, gorgeously trimmed with white ostrich plumes.

Grandpa and Grandma Graham graciously responded to a call to aid a family whose breadwinner had been badly mangled under a harrow when his six-horse team bolted and ran, frightened when the driver's hat blew off while he was untangling a horse that had stepped over its tug. The Grahams were needed for a long time; then they moved on to help with another family's predicament, and there was never question as to whether the Yeomans had dismissed the Grahams or the Grahams had quit the Yeomans. Quite plain to see, however, was the fact that Betty Yeoman needed no help to manage her part of the homestead's operations.

She measured the floors and ordered the Brussels carpet for the parlor and sitting room, and helped Abner tack it neatly wall to wall. She put him to the task of building corner cupboards for the sea shells and marine souvenirs she had collected on her visits to Seattle; and she faithfully carried her dishpan water three times daily to the rows of locust saplings she persuaded the elder Yeoman to plant for shade around the dooryard. She mothered her babies—Sue and Carl and tiny Meg, the pixie—like a bustling, fussy little red hen. When old Abner let his fondness for the youngsters lure him to the rash purchase of a whopping bag of jelly beans that produced three terrific tummie aches, Betty ruffled her feathers and squawked him a memorable scolding.

The year of the BIG CROP, the Yeomans bought their Model T touring car—and Ben proudly packed in the family and the big lunch basket and drove to the Fourth of July celebration in the county seat. When young Sue was chosen "Goddess of Liberty" and seated on a bunting-covered pedestal in the bandstand, her dimples winking from one cheek to the other and her brown curls making a pretty base for her red-white-and-blue crown, Ben and Betty beamed with pride and Grandpa Yeoman treated them all to ice-cream cones.

They worried about the big war. Sometimes it seemed as if Ben thought the world was challenging just him to put aside his farming and his family, and pick up a rifle and go settle the whole mess. But against this hot sting of patriotism pressed more sobering problems. The Allies needed food, and more food, and to produce it men like Ben had all they could do and more. "Food will win the war," the slogan said, and the Yeomans took it seriously. Betty "Hooverized" her canning, and for two years the peaches and the pears in her jars had a flat, sugar-lacking taste.

Young Carl was ten in the spring of 1918. That meant he had "come of age" for joining a 4-H Club. Under the sponsorship of the extension service of the Department of Agriculture, the 4-H Clubs guided boys and girls in completing projects such as raising calves and pigs and gardens for the boys, and sewing, canning and baking for the girls.

In the Yeoman barnyard that spring there was a runty little sow pig that tagged at Carl's heels every time he came near the herd. The boy befriended the little squealer, first with occasional apple cores, then with handouts from the feed bins. Soon the pig was a pet, and Carl began letting her out of the barnyard so she could follow him in his daily wanderings around the farm.

"Dad, do you think I could join the 4-H Club and raise a pig?" Carl asked at the supper table one evening. "I'm ten, you know—and that's how old you have to be."

"Well, Son, I think it could be arranged," his father replied. "What kind of a pig do you have in mind?"

"Tessabell!" the boy blurted.

"Who or what is Tessabell?" Ben asked.

"Oh, silly boy, he's calling his pig the same name that the girl had in that moving picture we saw last month," Sue explained. "She was 'Tess of the Storm Country'—remember?"

"Are you talking about that little runt that tags you around?" the father asked.

"Yep—but she won't be a runt after I take care of her," Carl promised.

"She's a scrubby pig," Sue said scornfully.

"She is not! She's sensible!" shouted the boy.

"Whoever heard of a sensible pig?"

Betty tapped her foot. "Stop this squabbling!" she demanded.

"Well, Carl, wouldn't it be better for us to pick out a real good pig for your project?" Ben suggested.

"She picked me out!" the boy declared. "And I'll bet she'll be the best pig this farm ever had."

"All right," his father said, "Tessabell is your pig, Carl, and now we'll see if you can make a fine, fat hog out of her."

Carl filled out his 4-H enrollment card and once a month he saddled his pony and rode to the courthouse for the junior livestock club's meeting. His club leader gave him a little book for keeping a record of the pounds of feed he used. Carl found an old kettle that held two pounds of rolled wheat and he

70

tacked a calendar above the feed bin so he could put a mark on the proper date each time he fed Tess a kettle of grain. First it was a kettle a day, then two, then three, and as the time for the county fair approached, Tess was eating five measures every day. And young Carl was right. She was, indeed, the biggest and best-looking hog in the Yeoman barnyard. Not only that, she won first prize at the county fair and sold for the fabulous price of $43.30.

The triumphs of Tess were a mixture of joy and sorrow for young Carl. He was very quiet riding home from the fair and when he put his pet hog's private trough away in the shed behind the granary, he lingered there alone a long time while big, hot tears streamed down his suntanned cheeks.

The next great event in Carl's young life came many months later. It was more exciting than anything he'd ever known. His father bought a tractor. A mechanic drove it out from town and spent half a day showing Ben how to start it and stop it, and how to convert some of the farm's horse-drawn equipment for attachment to the tractor's drawbar. This machine was one of Henry Ford's great ideas, and to Carl it looked like something very wonderful. Its wheels were painted red, the motor and frame gray, and it made almost as much noise as the separator of a threshing outfit roaring lustily beside a stack of wheat. Ben told Carl he could try the seat and see what it felt like to put his hands on the steering wheel while the motor idled. But he mustn't touch any of the levers, Ben cautioned. The boy eagerly climbed into the iron seat, gripped the wheel and looking ahead wide-eyed he imagined he was rushing down a strip of stubble with a deep, black furrow slithering open behind the big, cleated drive wheels. The boy got off, feeling as proud as a jockey who has just won the Derby.

71

Ben signaled to Abner to try the seat, too. The old man shrugged and shook his head. There was a cold breeze blowing across the fields, and Abner buttoned his mackinaw tight about his throat and fumbled for his handkerchief. The cold wind was making his eyes water, and he blinked and squinted hard as if trying to see something he wasn't quite sure was there. "Pa, be careful around those colts," his son had cautioned him a long time before. "They spook awful suddenly sometimes . . . and you can't tell what they'll do." Was that the caution that held the old man back—made him keep his distance from this new steel colt? "You can't tell what they'll do . . ."

Those words of warning were valid.

The arrival of the steel colt marked the transition from a horse-drawn to a horsepower farm economy. Ben's roaring motor standing there on its four bright red wheels was a mechanical package into which had been compressed four sturdy Percherons . . . or Belgians, Clydesdales or Shires. But its steel belly hungered for gasoline, not for the farm's own hay—and whatever its gender, it was never going to be the sire or dam of another tractor.

Abner didn't live to see what the mechanized farm would really face up to. More than thirty years before anybody heard of the word *agribusiness*, Abner Yeoman, old and weary, found his beloved farm engulfed in a strong current of change. For three centuries, the agricultural life of the Yeomans had been the same, generation after generation. It was life on a frontier, wild or tamed, but always earthbound . . . always a life devoted to supplying, producing and using most of the family's needs right there on the land that lay within the farm's line fences. Then suddenly it wasn't a frontier any more. The agriculture that beaconed men to its conquest on their boundaried pieces of land now was only a small part of a greater territory of opportunity, a vast new frontier where the outposts of the suppliers, the processors, the transporters, the traders and the distributors hummed with activity—busy as the land offices of the last earthbound frontier.

It was time now to watch the sunrise on a new frontier.

Part Two

THE
TRANSITION

➤➤➤➤➤➤➤➤➤➤➤➤➤➤➤➤➤➤➤➤➤➤➤➤➤➤➤➤➤➤➤➤➤➤➤➤

For two decades—approximately between 1920 and 1940—farmers were overwhelmed by problems and hardships that marked the beginning of the end of the Earthbound Era and the start of a new era in which businesses closely related to agriculture outgrew farming's contribution to the nation's economy. The new land frontier faded from the scene, and the frontier of economic progress shifted in such a way that farm families were suddenly and desperately confronted with the necessity of buying a modern standard of living instead of being able to create it to a considerable degree directly from the soil of their farms. More and more businesses appeared which furnished supplies to farms and which processed, stored and marketed farming's products. Combined with agriculture,

75

these businesses formed an economic unit which by mid-century became more than twice as big as agriculture. This set the stage for a new idea in respect to economics—the idea that agriculture has become an integral part of the agribusiness which now constitutes a major segment in the nation's economy.

THE FRONTIERS SHIFTED . . . but it was difficult to tell precisely when it happened. For two centuries and longer following the settlement at Jamestown, agriculture was the major economic entity. It was huge in its proportions of national employment and resources and opportunities. In comparison, the businesses providing it with supplies or using its overflow of abundance were like the trading posts in the wilderness. Every farm was its own small frontier, a territory within its boundary fences where a family produced and used most of what it required— the same way of life, generation after generation, whether working on old soil or pioneering on new land. And all the farms, added together, comprised the great earthbound frontier engaging a big percentage of the population, consuming

77

a large part of the production, affording a great many of the opportunities a man could find to assure his family a satisfactory, often enviable, standard of living.

But the business outposts of agriculture grew one by one, little by little, until the day came when they were as big as all of agriculture itself. The frontier had moved to the outposts, and agriculture and its earthbound farming was now becoming the lesser part of something bigger.

Exactly when this transition took place or what incident or development turned men's backs on the old frontier of earthbound farming and set them marching in an ever-swelling tide into the new frontier of agribusiness are points for the historians to ponder. It would depend on the factors one considered most important. If dollar economy were the yardstick, then one might say that the year when the off-farm businesses related to farming outgrew the dollar value of on-farm production was the year that the frontiers shifted. In an over-all sense, this might be acceptable, but a date thus selected might not fit very many of the different kinds and types of farming.

For instance, some kinds of farming were influenced greatly by agribusiness developments many years ago and have experienced no similarly significant changes for a very long time. Sheep raising is a good example. Its terrific agribusiness development came with the invention of power machinery for the textile industries more than a century ago, and after this took place nothing else so dynamic has affected sheep farming.

It's also true that some farming regions are influenced more than others by the transition from agriculture to agribusiness. There's a great contrast, for instance, in the agribusiness developments related to the grape-producing regions and the localities where soybeans are an important crop. Producing and marketing fresh grapes, raisins and wine involves a relatively simple pattern of supplies, processes and distribution—one that has been established for a long time and has undergone only minor changes—whereas soybeans, which were unimportant in America prior to World War I, have undergone an extremely complex agribusiness development, one that still is constantly changing and expanding.

The spasmodic impacts of agribusiness in the first three centuries of American agriculture were cushioned by our expanding frontier of new farm land. This earthbound frontier absorbed great increases in our population; gave security and stability to farming as an occupation; and sufficed to answer the individual's quest for a place to create a relatively good standard of living.

But Abner was the last generation of the Yeoman family to find it so. His nearly eighty years of life had carried him to the end of an era, and the years that rounded out a century from the date of his birth hastened the transition to farming's new era—the agribusiness era.

When his father's estate was settled, Ben Yeoman knew very well that he had much for which to be grateful. Through his years of partnership in farming with his father, and by inheritance, he was now the sole owner of 320 acres—as fine a farm as any on this broad prairie. His house was spacious and sound. Down to the last months of his life, Abner had made his regular rounds with hammer, saw and paintbrush, methodically keeping the premises repaired and attractive. Ben had barns and sheds to shelter all his stock and equipment . . . and the merit of every item, implement or animal, was good. A hundred of his 250 tillable acres was green with its new crop. He held warehouse receipts for 500 bushels of last year's wheat, and the granary on the farm was bulging with several hundred more to feed or sell. The year was 1920 . . . Ben owed no debts . . . and wheat was $2.50 per bushel!

Leaning on his dooryard gate, Ben looked out across his fields, and the view was pleasant.

"Betty, come out here a minute, please," he called to his wife, who was busy with the morning's kitchen chores.

"What is it, Ben?" she asked, stepping outside where the spring sunshine blinked lightly from the gray strands in the coil of red braids wrapped and pinned about her head.

"You see that hill over there by the Bonner place?" Ben pointed.

"Of course I see it. I look at it a thousand times a day," she answered.

"Well, Honey, we ought to own all of it instead of just one side."

"Why so?"

"It's because of the tractor," Ben explained.

"What does the tractor have to do with owning a whole hill?" Betty challenged.

"The tractor's not as simple to use as a team," Ben began. "Going back and forth along one side is a nuisance . . . and dangerous, too. But if I could spiral round and round, it would be a lot better."

"Well, that much of it seems to make sense," Betty commented.

"I just got to thinkin'," Ben went on. "Old Man Bonner left that eighty acres to his daughter who lives back East. I'll bet she'd be glad to sell it."

"Maybe not so glad, with wheat two-fifty a bushel," Betty said.

"That's why now's such a good time to buy it. A few crops

and we'd have it paid off ... even at a good, stiff price for it," Ben enthused.

Bonner's daughter was no fool. Whereas $75 an acre was a pretty good price for this dry prairie land, with half the ground carrying a crop for the new owner, she set her price at $100 an acre. To make the deal, Ben and Betty paid $1,000 down and gave her a mortgage for $7,000 to run seven years, to 1928, at 6 per cent interest.

Ben was very happy. The tractor pulled its plow neatly around the bottom of the hill, and the furrows began to spiral upward toward the summit. But sometimes the tractor balked. Its fuel system behaved all right on level ground, but when the machine was tilted on a hillside it often required a lot of tinkering and some pretty bad words to get it moving after it stopped. Sometimes Ben had to hike back to the barn, harness a team and, riding one of the horses bareback, go out and tow the tractor off the hillside to a favorable starting position. There were times, too, when the tractor just would not respond to any amount of cranking, and Carl would be late for school because his father needed him to man the tractor's controls while Ben drove a four-horse hitch to tow the balky machine—a risky but sometimes effective way to get it started.

Funny thing, the tractor was supposed to speed up farm work, to help a man accomplish a lot more than he could with his horses. For a long time, however, the skeptics were betting on the horse, not on the tractor that first appeared on the farms. By the time Ben was fretting over his tractor's cantankerous behavior, the mobile traction engine had more than sixty years of hopes and disappointments behind it. As early as 1858, J. W. Fawkes developed a steam engine that pulled eight plows at a speed of three miles an hour in heavy sod. Almost twenty years later Otto received his patents for an internal-combustion engine, and thirteen years later farm-equipment makers were installing this type of engine on rigs designed to pull heavy loads. The word "tractor" wasn't tossed into the language until 1906 when a salesman hit upon it as a short way to say "gasoline traction engine." In another ten years, the country saw scores of companies try their hand at tractor design, manufacturing and selling. At first the aim had been to make a tractor so large and powerful that it would do the work of the multiple horse and mule hitches used on the biggest grain ranches; then suddenly the effort shifted to making a small, handy tractor that would serve the general farmer. Now the idea was to make a machine that was faster, more powerful than a team of horses . . . and something that didn't have to be fed, stable-cleaned and groomed when it wasn't working. This was the idea that appealed to Ben—but he kept all of his horses, just in case it didn't work out according to plan; and often it did not.

Before Ben's new field on the hill was plowed, the price of wheat slid down from its $2.50 peak. He sold his warehoused holdings for $2.00. Meg, his youngest daughter, was rushed to Portland for an appendix operation, and when the bills came in they made a big dent in the cash received for the wheat. But the outlook wasn't too bad. New land and all, Ben had 130 acres of wheat to harvest. Even at a skimpy ten bushels to the acre, with wheat around $2.00, this year would see the farm's biggest wheat income. Add to that the receipts for fruit and livestock—several hundred dollars, most years since the war—and it was a rather rosy picture, Ben assured himself. Perhaps, though, it would be wise to sell his spring pigs after they had gained a few pounds gleaning lost wheat from his stubble fields rather than to use good wheat to finish them for market. Better to have about $500 worth of wheat in his own granary than to stake it on fattening a carload of pigs at a time when hog prices were on the skids, Ben decided.

By the time the big steam threshing outfit began making its rounds of the community's grain stacks the price of wheat sank below $2.00. The market jittered up or down a cent or two almost every day, but at the end of nearly every week it was lower than it had been the previous week. The wheat growers were uneasy, and as the weeks passed, Ben was aware that the price declines were taking hundred-dollar bites out of his anticipated income—a situation that made him desperately anxious to sell his crop as soon as possible.

For years Ben had worked alone hauling the farm's wheat to the warehouse that stood beside the town's railroad station. He would load two wagons in a tandem hitch and pull them to town with six big draft horses. One trip made a hard day's work when added to his regular chores. Sometimes rain or the farm's other projects interrupted the routine of a daily trip and it might take two or three weeks for Ben to deliver all of his wheat to the warehouse. This year, however, taking so long to deliver his crop could be very costly. When Ben learned that he could hire men with motor trucks to haul his entire crop in two days, he didn't hesitate to accept their proposition. The way he figured it, he might easily lose more money from falling prices while he was doing the hauling himself than the cost of paying the truckers for their faster services.

He was right, but just the same a new and big item appeared in the list of farm expenses—the truckers' bill.

Ben took the warehouse receipts out of his wallet and Betty pushed the supper dishes aside. She brought Abner's ancient gray ledger and a pad of writing paper to the table. Ben read the figures and his wife briskly proceeded with the arithmetic.

"Why, Ben, we had a wonderful crop!" she exclaimed. "It's

83

more than two thousand bushels and the yield was fourteen bushels to the acre. You said it was only going to be ten."

"I didn't want to get our hopes too high," Ben said. Then he drew out of his wallet the deposit slip—$3,780.37. "For a little while, we're rich, Honey."

It was for a very little while.

When Ben began seeding his new crop that fall, he discovered that the farm's old grain drill, designed to be horse-drawn, could not stand the wear and tear resulting from the tractor's greater speed. Buying a new drill added another big figure to the farm's expenses. The new equipment, however, plus the tractor's fast pace across the fields, brought joy to Ben's heart as he whizzed through the planting of the acreage on the homestead. Then he quickly finished the additional field on the Bonner place, doing it all in less time than it used to take the horses to cover only three-fourths as much land. The bill for gasoline, however, became rather substantial.

The money banked from the wheat crop melted to less than $3,000 after bills for the trucking, the new grain drill and the gasoline were paid. Abner's old windmill took a balky streak, and the bills for replacing gears and blacksmithing the worn old parts melted a few hundreds from the bank account. Forty rods of woven wire fencing to replace a tumble-down stretch of board fencing on the Bonner place subtracted hundreds more. Now the remaining wheat receipts were less than $2,000. Ben sold his half-grown pigs off the stubble for enough to lift the balance once more above the $2,000 mark. There had been only languid interest in the farm's fruit this season, and Betty had managed to trade most of the output to the grocer. The small amount of cash sales vanished in payment for the family's living expenses. Ben watched the wheat market dip lower and lower—rejoicing that he had the good fortune to cash in quickly as soon as his crop had been harvested, but worrying, too, about the unpleasant outlook.

Spring brought soft, warm winds, yellow daffodils around the farm house, and interest on the mortgaged Bonner property and taxes on the farm's real estate. Now last year's income had melted down below the $1,000 mark. After the children were in bed, the late hours of the evening found Ben and Betty discussing money problems. Betty argued that it would be best to pinch and scrape enough to pay the $1,200 that would be necessary each year if they were to have the Bonner mortgage amortized on schedule over six years. But Ben could see that with gasoline to buy, truckers to hire, and new, more costly repairs and equipment demanding large but handy sums of money, subtracting $1,200 from their resources was going to be mighty painful. Actually, Ben and his wife never reached a decision—they paid the mortgage interest and that was all. Later, perhaps, paying an installment on the mortgage could follow some upturn of their income prospects. Always there were consoling possibilities turning over in Ben's mind. A good team of Percherons was usually considered worth four or five hundred dollars, and with the tractor doing a good bit of the field work, there was hardly any need for twelve big draft horses. There was just one good reason to hesitate, however, Ben reminded himself whenever selling horses came to mind. All twelve horses had been foaled on the farm and each was a family pet in every sense of the word. Selling one of them would be like selling a member of the family.

The old windmill gave up the ghost right in the midst of the busy season for plowing and harrowing. All its parts were obsolete, and taking down the old machine and putting up a new one involved a costly, time-consuming feat of engineering. An easier solution was to retire the old machine and install a gasoline engine to power the pump. This Ben did ... and now only a few hundred dollars remained of last year's crop money.

It was time now to sell the wheat in the farm's granary, but, alas, this was 1921 and the market was less than $1.00 a bushel.

The new crop sulked and made a halfhearted show of producing a respectable yield. Ben remembered how lucky he had been to sell his crop quickly after last year's harvest and he repeated the program—but this time he caught the low mark of the season—sixty cents a bushel. When he showed Betty the bank deposit slip, the figures for the year's wheat crop were just a little under $1,100. When the bills for threshing, trucking and gasoline were paid, Ben and Betty Yeoman had very little left from their year's operations. Now to meet the interest payments and the taxes, money had to come out of the meager savings account they had started for educating the children.

A man busy with spring plowing in a big wheat field usually works all day without having visitors approach him, but when a car stops by the side of the road and the man gets out and walks across the field's dusty furrows, his mission is usually important. Ben saw the car stop and he recognized the stocky figure of the threshing contractor, Ole Johnson. Ole waddled toward the tractor. Ben calculated the spot where he could stop and give Ole the benefit of the shortest distance, and there he threw the tractor out of gear and let it idle. Ole sauntered up and leaned heavily on the tractor's gas tank, huffing and puffing. When he got his breath, he said it was a good day for plowing and Ben said, yes, the weather had been pretty good this spring.

Then Ole said, "Ben, I've sold my threshing outfit to a feller 'way over in the east end of the county. I can't compete with the combines. Now that they're makin' the smaller ones, every farmer figures he'll have one of his own. Six farms on my threshing circuit put 'em in last year. There just weren't enough farms left in my circuit to keep me going. Thought I'd better get around and tell my old customers early-like so they'll have time to make other arrangements."

"Gosh, that's quite a surprise," Ben said when Ole ran out of breath. "I always figured death, taxes and Johnson's threshing bill were in the same class—permanent, that is."

"Oh, I seen it comin' for a long time," Ole replied. "Them combines—first time I seen one of them, I says to myself, 'Ole, that's got your thresher beat forty ways for Sunday'—and I got the itch to buy myself one of 'em. But they was just big ones at that time. Took twenty or thirty horses to pull 'em. 'Now look here, Ole,' I says to myself, 'you can't turn one of them big outfits around twice in fields the size they got around here.' So I kept on with my thresher."

"What are you going to do now, Ole?" Ben asked. "You've got wheat of your own to thresh."

"Well, now, I sure have," Ole said, chuckling, "and the thing I'm a-goin' to do is buy me one of them small combines. And a tractor to drag her around. No horses for me, brother. I'm too fat to wrestle with a manure fork any more."

"Then are you going to do custom harvesting with your combine?" Ben asked.

"Only for my two brothers," Ole replied. "These machines like I'm gettin' are too small to harvest more than maybe eight hundred acres in a season. Take on too much, and you make customers mad. 'Tain't like threshin'—with the grain safe in the stack for maybe a month or more. You gotta do your combinin' before grain shatters or the customer's a-goin' to be awful sore."

"Guess we'll have to go back to the old ways, like when I

was a kid," Ben observed. "Neighbors chipped in together and bought a machine; everybody got in the act and we had big work crews . . . and, best of all, no wages to pay."

"Forget it! That system's no good any more," Ole declared. "Long as you could patch a machine with a piece of haywire or a bandage of rawhide there wasn't too much cussin' over who broke what, but, man alive, when a ten-dollar gear busts on a neighborhood-owned grain drill, or hay baler, or somethin' like that, there's hell to pay."

"I know what you mean," Ben admitted.

"And swap work—like the old folks did?" Ole spat his tobacco juice down-wind. "Huh!" he exclaimed. "There ain't the same at-tude as there used to be. Take a threshin' crew. Tender gets six bucks; jigger gets five; sewers, four-fifty; forkers, three bucks. So what happens? Nobody'll swap his time, even-steven, for the other feller's—and nobody wants one of the bum jobs and to have to pay a cash difference to the others when the crew works for him. Next thing you know, neighbors ain't speakin' t'one 'nother, let alone workin' together."

Ole plodded off, then turned and shouted, "Better get your own combine, Ben."

A combine, just a small combine, costs a lot of money, Ben would have answered, but Ole was too far away to hear him. Looking back to check the set of his plow, Ben saw a small brown field mouse running along the smooth trough of the furrow. It came straight toward the plow, sometimes hurrying, sometimes hesitating as if preoccupied, confused. It reached the steel of the plowshare, then reversed its course and sped down the furrow, only to turn suddenly and come hopping toward the plow again. Under his breath Ben was saying, "Same soil, same field, my little mouse, but, gosh, how fast things can change and mix you up!"

The tractor needed new parts; in fact, it needed a complete overhaul. That was a normal occurrence in the operation of a gasoline motor, Ben understood, and it was not cause for the apprehensive, half-doomed feeling that clutched at his spirits whenever he considered his tractor's condition. Now, as he set it in gear and gunned the motor, he thought about a combine . . . thought about the pathetic, mixed-up mouse, and again about a combine . . . and it seemed to Ben as if every connecting rod were clattering on worn-out bearings, every turn of the transmission a threat of screeching ruin, every revolution of the drive wheels a lurching rush toward some kind of financial catastrophe. The foreboding mood lasted while he made several turns around the field, but at last he had formed a plan: He would not mention the threshing problem to Betty until after the tractor was repaired . . . and the bill paid.

But how silly can a man be? He was rinsing the soap from the back of his neck, and the splash of the water and the thumping of the basin on the wood shelf beside the kitchen sink made noise enough to smother some of Betty's chatter but not the words "Johnson sold his thresher."

"How'd you hear about that?" Ben asked, but he knew the answer—the party telephone line, of course. He rubbed the towel about his ears, blotted his eyes, and rubbed his neck and ears again while he fumbled for a good way to proceed with the subject of combines. Again it was Betty who hurdled his confusion with a surprising remark.

"The Browns are buying a combine and they'd like to contract to cut our crop—just ours—so they'll have just enough to make the machine pay, but not more than they can cut in good season." Betty's voice had a reassuring, jubilant note.

Ben blinked. He struggled to suppress an exclamation of relief. Waiting a moment, he managed to put a taciturn mask over his comment. "How much per acre?"

"They want five dollars," Betty answered.

"Five dollars!" Ben exclaimed. "That'll cost us six or seven hundred dollars. We'd better buy our own combine," he blustered.

"Yes, I know, dear. Except that a combine costs four thousand two hundred and ninety-five dollars," she chided. "I think, perhaps, it would be wise for you to see Jim Brown before someone else gets in ahead of you."

With the idea that a friendly gift can say more than words, Ben put a box of dried prunes on the seat of the Model T next morning and drove over to the Browns. He was back at his plowing by ten o'clock . . . and Betty had given him a bright smile of approval when she put the pencil-written combining contract in the back pages of the old gray ledger. The agreed-upon price, she noted, was $4.75 per acre.

The tractor's crank shaft broke and the block cracked when Ben still had forty-five acres to plow . . . and nearly 150 acres to harrow. The repairs kept the tractor out of operation for more than a month—because old tractors from a score of farms were having breakdowns that spring and the dealer's service crew was swamped with work. Ben put his teams to use once more. Often his work was interrupted by a visitor who wanted to borrow horses to take the place of a tractor temporarily, but lending teams was one thing Ben Yeoman would not do. Then the same men began visiting a second time. Now they were wanting to buy horses. Ben said he wanted $400 for a team

. . . and the visitors went their way without bothering to "dicker."

Twice a week Ben would phone the dealer and inquire when his tractor would be ready to use. "The parts ought to be here next week" was the usual answer. One day Ben asked how much the repairs were going to cost. The dealer's reply was embellished with a long preamble full of technical phrases about parts and mechanic's methods, and the substance of the answer was about $300. Betty heard Ben repeat the figure with an exclamation of dismay, but she made no comment at the time.

A day later, as the family was finishing the evening meal, she said, "It seems to me the folks on this farm must make up their minds about something. Either we are going to be horse farmers or we are going to be tractor farmers—we can't be both and have enough money to make ends meet."

"The tractor's the coming thing," young Carl said.

"But you have to buy tractors, and we can raise our own colts. Why don't we raise colts any more, Daddy?" Sue asked.

"I guess it's because we haven't needed any, Sue," her father replied. "But come to think of it, there isn't a good draft stallion left on the prairie."

"Well," Betty said, keeping her voice calm and matter-of-fact, "this may be the last good chance to sell horses. Nearly every farm around us has a tractor now, and some farms don't have a horse on the place. This spell of breakdowns isn't going to last . . . we can be pretty sure of that. Maybe before better tractors come along, we should part with some of our twelve horses."

"Not Molly and Dolly!" Sue exclaimed.

"Probably not," Ben partially agreed. "I suppose we should

sell off the oldest teams first—but one sure gets attached to the old pets."

"We could sell enough to buy a new tractor," Carl proposed.

Next day the horse-hunting visitors began showing up again. They followed one another like people with aching teeth keeping their dentist's appointment—but this was rural courtesy rather than the result of an organized schedule. One could look for miles across the prairie and see when Ben had stopped his work to receive a visitor. As soon as he was plowing again, another caller who had arrived by flivver might be waiting as the tractor rounded the field, or if a competitor had arrived ahead of him, he just drove on, biding his turn. Before noon, Ben realized that the horse-hunters had been tipped off to a change of policy on the Yeoman homestead, and he smiled to himself at the way Betty had exploited a casual remark over the country telephone line to do a bit of advertising. The horse-hunters knew that the time had come for them to "dicker" with Ben . . . and "dicker" they did.

Ben's opening comments that he and his father had bred up the farm's horses until they reckoned every team on the place was worth $500 were received with respectful silence. When he "allowed" that the horse market wasn't what it used to be, his visitors responded with long stories about horse bargains they had been told were available in places scattered from Canada to Mexico. They tactfully "allowed" they hadn't seen the horses—implying, of course, that Ben's probably were better—but they were clever in hammering home the idea that one could buy a pretty good horse for less than $50.

Ben tried to sell Snow and Rain, the oldest pair, white with age, though once—and it seemed such a little while ago—they had been a handsome team of spunky, dappled, dark-gray colts, but the horse-hunters showed no interest. Finally, after much sparring in their bid and asked prices, Ben sold the bay geldings, Rex and Royal, his second oldest team, for $150. Then another buyer paid $175 for Pal and Pet . . . and while he fumbled with his billfold, he blurted, "A hundred dollars for the old, white team; take it or leave it while I'm counting the dough." Ben took it.

In the days that followed, Ben had a few offers for his younger teams, but none for more than $100. To Ben, these bids were ridiculous, if not to say, insulting. The six big Percherons stayed in Ben's alfalfa pasture—handsome and fat, sleek and lazy. His choring shifted from the daily routine of cleaning stables, grooming and harnessing horses, to cleaning spark plugs, washing black grease from springs and gears with kerosene, hammering stubborn metals that came hissing and red from his small forge. The barn smell had gone from his clothes and in its place was the odor of petroleum. Grease and carbon soiled his denims as fast as Betty could wash them . . . and the black grime made an ugly pattern in the creases of his hands, a black crescent under each fingernail, the indelible tattoo of the tractor farmer.

Always it seemed the repair of a motor or an implement began with the teasing prospect of a quick and easy fix-up, then slowly and stubbornly grew to proportions that consumed hours and sometimes days to finish the undertaking.

It was Abner's bountiful orchard that first made Ben aware of the way that the expanded operations initiated by the tractor were robbing time from other operations on the farm. It had taken the bugs and fungi nearly thirty years to find Abner's fruit trees and berry bushes, but now a long list of them held conventions in the Yeoman trees and vines. Old Abner lived to see only the first onslaughts of the pests. He

93

bought a wheelbarrow spray rig, a few simple chemicals, and methodically counterattacked. Ben and Carl took up the battle for a year or two, but that was while the tractor was new and better behaved. The county agent had mailed Ben a bulletin about pests and the sprays that discouraged their ravages. A check on the list of chemicals to buy and their costs, however, produced an easy decision. Ben had neither the time nor the cash to give his orchard proper protection. Now, when the early apples were ripening, Betty and their daughters would fill many baskets and lug them to the kitchen where they would sort out the best fruit, trim out the worm holes and after they salvaged enough for a few quarts of sauce, there would be bushels of waste remaining for Carl to carry to his pigs.

The year Ben sold his shoats instead of fattening them marked a change in the farm's livestock program. It had been Ben's intention to sell wheat at a high price that fall—but the price wasn't high. Now wheat was hovering around a dollar a bushel, but the need for quick conversion to cash kept him from holding wheat to feed hogs, although anyone could see that there were times when hogs brought more for wheat than one could get in the grain market. So Ben gave his four grade sows and the boar to Carl and the boy traded them all for a registered Berkshire-bred gilt. Ben was shocked at such a deal, but Betty said, "Never mind. The boy's only doing what the experts say: 'If you're going to raise stock, raise the best.' "

When his gilt had her litter, Carl advertised his pigs in the state farm paper and orders came for weanlings to be shipped to places scattered all over the state. One day the boy solemnly presented his father with a check for wheat he was feeding from the farm's granary, and Ben found himself bewildered by a mixture of surprise, pride and embarrassment. A year

later, Carl announced that he had $200 in his savings account—
$200 toward his college education.

Carl's money came from his sale of registered pigs, his prizes
won in 4-H Club livestock shows and his earnings during
school vacations. Ben didn't pay his son cash wages, but they
worked out an exchange of wheat for labor during the summer months when Carl spent long days, long weeks, working
on the home place. Carl used the wheat to grow his purebred
pigs. His last two vacations from high school, the boy worked
for combine owners, earning top wages as a sack sewer on their
machines. In the fall of 1926, Carl had $500 in his savings. Now
he was ready to enroll in the agriculture course at the State
College. He sold all of his hogs except a choice trio of his
breeding stock which he left in his father's care. Then he
packed his new cowhide suitcase and said "so-long" to family
and farm.

Ben sold his wheat for less than a dollar a bushel that fall . . .
and for the sixth time, the farm's income was too skimpy to
permit making a thousand-dollar payment on the mortgage
on the Bonner land. The years were speeding along. There
had been no BIG CROP and no BIG PRICE to give Ben's farming
headway toward a better financial situation.

Carl came home for his summer vacation and headed straight
for the pigpens. He selected a young boar which he placed
in a pen by itself. "Why such a special arrangement for him?"
Ben asked.

"Well, Dad," the boy replied, "I've got a good prospect interested in him . . . if he turns out like I hope he will. You see,
I met one of the real high-class breeders at a college meeting
and I talked up a sale, I hope."

"Couple of weeks ago, I offered him to a neighbor for ten
dollars," Ben confessed.

"I'm sure glad you didn't sell him," the youth remarked.

As the weeks passed, Ben was amazed by Carl's diligence. No matter how early or late the lad worked in the fields, he fed and exercised the boar as if it were the horse considered the year's most promising entry in the Kentucky Derby. Then one day a light truck carrying a hog crate drove into the Yeoman lane. When the truck left, the boar's pen was empty.

"See you sold your boar today," Ben remarked at supper that evening.

"Yep—for two hundred dollars," Carl said in a calm, casual voice. The women squealed, and Ben let out a low whistle. Then the youth laid the check on the supper table and patted it affectionately. "Look here, folks—this money goes for the down payment on a new car. We've had that shabby old flivver long enough."

Ben sputtered in protest, Sue and Meg gasped and Betty began to cry softly. But Carl was adamant.

"I'm going to buy the car this week, or bust," he declared. "And don't say I need it for college expenses. I've got jobs there that will see me through okay."

Spurred by the boy's generosity, the Yeomans all began to uncover small caches of savings to add to Carl's contribution. Betty took an envelope from the bottom of the drawer that held her cookbooks and displayed a packet of ten-dollar bills—$310 she had saved from the farm's "fruit money." And Sue produced $30—her "chicken money" from her 4-H poultry projects. Meg opened a purse with $12.80 in change—the money she earned in taking magazine subscriptions. Then Ben said, well, maybe they'd all end up in the poorhouse, but he'd dig up the rest to make the full payment on a new small car. For a week the Yeomans looked at the new models. They rode with the dealers and studied the advertising folders. Supper table conversation was lively now, with talk about wonderful things such as speedometers and "streamlining" and gear ratios. Finally, it was a green Chevie that won the family's heart . . . and for a long time whoever wrote to Carl at college began the letter with a faithful report on the Chevie's condition.

The fabulous price for the pig and the possession of the new car were the only bright spots in a long stretch of dreary, disappointing years for the Yeoman family. In his fiftieth year, Ben found himself puzzling as to why his life now was so different than when he was a younger man. The years had not robbed him of health or strength. He was not lazy—in fact, he was putting more and more effort in his work, driving himself in an unrelenting desire to achieve his ambition to make his farm a model of progressive development. There had been a time, he could well remember, when it seemed that everything he and his father undertook resulted in improvement, achievement, progress. Work made growth; created beauty; brought rich rewards in all-around satisfaction and well being. Big and discouraging tasks melted away little by little, and each day's accomplishment, however small, showed the promise of bringing desires a mite closer to fulfillment.

Not so any more. The header, rusting in the old log shed, was a sort of symbol for the change. The farm had reached the peak of its development when the header was used for harvesting. Now forsaken and neglected, the header seemed to be communicating its mood to the rest of the farm. The roof over its shed sagged when one of its pole rafters had cracked under the weight of a deep, wet snow. Ben was too busy to fix it. Then the roof collapsed and the shed became an eyesore. Old rails rotted in the fences; the once strong, straight fences of the barnyard were tilted and pushed out of line by the stock,

97

and planks were broken and hastily patched by nailing on whatever size or shape of board came to hand. The orchard went without its annual pruning; dead limbs and even some dead trees made it look shabby and run-down; thistles and milk-weeds grew tall amidst the berry bushes and the grapevines. The house needed paint and there were shingles demanding attention. For a while, Betty made lists of the things needing repair—and Ben would carry her notes in his shirt pocket until the next washing.

Sometimes he freed himself from the machines long enough to get a nail bucket and a hammer and really tear into a repair job. Always, however, more was falling apart than he was fixing, and strive as he would, Ben could not restore the tidy, prosperous look the farm had in Abner's time.

The deterioration of the buildings, fences, equipment and the orchard was disheartening enough—but along with it came a stealthy undermining of the Yeomans' standard of living. Now that Sue and Meg were attending the community's consolidated high school, the long bus trips to and from town used up the hours they had spent on their 4-H poultry and food conservation projects. Ben insisted that Betty had work enough without caring for the chickens. He'd do it, he said. But with his mind on a balky carburetor or a bracket to blacksmith, Ben forgot his poultry chores too often and the hens ceased to lay. Buying store eggs was the first retreat on the food front. It was followed by store bacon . . . by store potatoes . . . and by dried prunes packed in California.

Often Ben and Betty discussed this lamentable departure from the provident abundance of food the farm had once supplied. Sometimes their tempers flared over the reasons, the excuses, the alternatives taken, that explained a phase of what was happening. Of course, Ben was busy as blazes every day.

Of course, Betty was thrifty, hard-working and conscientious. What then explained the insidious, persistent downward trend of their standard of living? Why could not their farm, with its more efficient implements, now provide as prosperous a living as the Yeomans had enjoyed ten or twenty years before?

One reason was the overlapping of the old order and the new order. The Yeomans were slow to abandon the horses . . . so they had the same old routine of barn chores, plus the new routine of machinery care. Adjustments to make his work habits conform to mechanized farming were long overdue before Ben fully applied them. A tractor farmer needed to eliminate the puttering sort of tasks or get them out of the way well ahead of the time to use the tractor, for in its early forms this machine had to be humored (tinkered and perhaps repaired) or it would sulk, and gone would be the hours when it might have accomplished the most usefulness.

And that brings out another reason why the tractor didn't make it easier to produce more things the family wanted for food. The early tractor was temperamental. It had steel wheels, and on muddy ground these would skid and play tricks on the driver. Even a wet spot that the plow team would slosh through was as treacherous for a tractor as a pit-type trap. Sometimes Ben spent several hours rescuing his mired machine. When the going was good, the tractor was faster than horses—but sometimes the tractor's performance was like the hare's, a good team like the tortoise's, in a race to get the season's work done on time. And, of course, Ben—as did all tractor owners—expected the machine would enable him to operate on a larger scale. In his zeal to make the most of this expectation, he was prone to attempt too much. Consequently Ben spent more time in the fields and less around the farmstead doing the things Abner used to do for a good living. The early tractor was a specialized machine intended for enlarging the operations to produce a particular crop, and in doing this, it kept the farmer away from the diversity of projects that embellished the family's food supply.

Man's labor on the farm had taken on a new obligation—and perhaps that explained the changes. When earthbound agriculture was in full flower a stallion and a mare could provide a colt . . . and the sunshine, the rain and the farm's own soil could provide the forage to grow the colt to harness age . . . and the farm's pasture, grain and hay could provide the energy that gave the horse the power to work. Man's labor, aiding these natural processes, created the farm's power units, the teams of horses that made productive agriculture possible. But now man's labor was obligated to create the money that would buy the tractor, buy the fuel that powered it. Ben Yeoman's labor, in effect, had to be sold off the farm now for enough money to buy the engine and fuel that replaced the horse and the hay.

It was not exactly as simple as this, but a great deal of the story was told in one sentence. Tractors don't eat hay.

7.

THE TIME had arrived when the development of the new frontier, the agribusiness frontier, was rapidly sapping the self-sufficiency out of the old earthbound frontier. The family on a farm could no longer provide most of its essential supplies inside the limits of its boundary fences . . . nor could it live now in a relatively smug state of prosperity, sustaining this good standard of living largely by consuming what it produced from its own acres.

To describe what was happening on the farm, one might say that the explosions inside the cylinders of a gasoline engine were blowing apart an old way of life. There were, of course, other forces contributing to the changes, but none had more dramatic impact than the automobile and the tractor. Like the progress from dirt-floored cabin to clapboard cottage . . . from buckskin breeches to tailored suit . . . from oiled-paper windows to glass panes . . . the shift from horse-and-buggy to automobile was a milestone on the road to better living. And like the steps from scythe to reaper . . . from flail to threshing machine . . . the tractor excelled the horse in expanding the farm's productivity. Either a farm family was to march in step with this parade of progress or it was bound to suffer the privations of the backward.

It was a long time before people realized that earthbound agriculture could not keep the farm family in step with American progress. Again it was the gasoline engine, on the highway and in the field, that so clearly illustrated the way agriculture was reaching the limits of self-sufficiency. Farming's progress led to demand for the tractor and the fuel to run it, but since neither the machine nor the petroleum could be created from the farm's own soil, agriculture was forced to concede a reduction of its self-sufficiency and turn to enterprises outside of its own versatility to provide both tractors and gasoline. This was, indeed, a major compromise because the price of a tractor was equal to a relatively large part of a farm's capital—and the cost of tractor fuel became a similarly big portion of a farm's operating expenses. Simultaneously on the income side of the equation, the tractor helped to build up a surplus, first by not consuming grain and hay and secondly by improving farming methods. This surplus, in turn, had the effect of beating down price and further reducing net income.

While the business aspects of agriculture were thus being compromised by an ever-increasing dependence on off-farm sources of essential supplies, now also the satisfactions of a way of life on the farm were becoming dependent on resources outside of agriculture. It could be argued that the automobile was not an essential part of a farm's operating facilities, but one must remember that before the motorcar appeared a very desirable standard of living could be almost entirely farm-made. In other words, during the earthbound era, agriculture by itself could produce a highly satisfactory standard of living. The gasoline engine, however, brought a new standard into general acceptance, and for a farm family to live without an automobile meant that it was retarded to a substandard way of life. To enable farm people to live in harmony with the changing standards, agriculture now had to provide compensation that would make it possible for them to buy life's embellishments from off-farm sources.

This required money.

Ben Yeoman adjusted the flame of the kerosene lamp on the sitting-room table and opened the farm's well-worn ledger. Betty rummaged in a cupboard drawer for an old school tablet, muttering that no one ever bothered to sharpen a pencil except her.

"Here, let me have it," Ben proposed. He fished in his trouser pocket for his jackknife and, taking the stubby pencil, walked to the tall cast-iron stove at the side of the room. He lifted the stove door handle with his foot and began whittling the pencil's point, trying dexterously to aim the flying chips into the red embers of the evening's wood fire.

Betty chuckled. "Well, you steered a few of them through the door," she said. Ben's frown softened to a pleasant grin as he handed her the sharp-pointed pencil. He sat down wearily and the frown returned.

The year was 1928; the month was January. In three more months the seven years of the Bonner mortgage would come to an end. All of the $7000 principal remained outstanding and the whole of it would be due and payable when the seven years were up. The high hopes of Ben and Betty to have paid off a thousand dollars each year had blighted and died.

"Let's check back and see what happened," Ben suggested. "We'll begin with the year we bought the Bonner place." So he thumbed the pages and read the figures while Betty copied them in a column on the tablet paper. Sometimes he paused to comment about unusual figures—large ones if they were expenses, small ones if they were crop receipts. Occasionally his comment drew fire from Betty. He should have done this, or he should have done that, she said. "No use scolding now," Ben reminded her.

Their gross cash income ranged between $1500 and $2700 . . . and it averaged $2164. Their operating expenses ranged from $1300 to $2300, the differences from year to year being due to ability to pay rather than to fluctuations in costs, but the average was $1678.

"That means we had just $486 a year to live on. No wonder we couldn't pay a thousand dollars a year on a mortgage!" Betty exclaimed.

"It's plain to see we couldn't," Ben replied.

He slid his reading glasses down his nose and looked at his wife over the tops of the lenses. "Well, Bet, what's the next move?"

She drummed the tablet with the tip of the pencil. "One thing's very plain—we need money," she said.

They discussed turning the eighty acres back to Bonner's daughter. Obviously, she could foreclose the mortgage and repossess them—but, of course, there was no point in putting her to all that legal rigmarole. Better to deed them back to her and say they were sorry it had to be that way. But it did sting the Yeomans' pride to think that all the neighbors would know they had failed to meet a financial obligation. Betty suggested that they might try to negotiate a deal at a lower price, but Ben said he didn't like such tactics. "That would make us look like a pair of sharpies," he said.

"Then why not ask if we can rent them?" Betty proposed. "She would get a third of the wheat crop as rent and we'd have no interest, taxes or installments to pay."

"That's a better idea," Ben agreed.

Miss Bonner, who was an instructor in a girls' school in the East, engaged one of the town's lawyers to handle her western property interests. Clay Benton was a grim-visaged, round-shouldered, lean young man. When Betty and Ben Yeoman entered his small, shabby office over the town's bank, his curt manner gave no lift to their sagging spirits. Benton had a way of jabbing at things, such as the chair he offered Betty and the folder he took out of a file, that put one on guard. He would flick the papers in the folder as if each one deserved his special scorn.

"Well, as you know," Ben began, "we have not been able to pay Miss Bonner anything on the principal. We've barely been able to keep up the taxes and pay the interest."

"So?" Benton's query was in a tone that seemed to anticipate the proposal Ben was about to make.

"There's not much else we can do except give Miss Bonner a deed and say we're sorry," Ben continued.

"I'm afraid it's not as simple as that," Benton said bluntly.

"I don't quite understand," Betty spoke timidly.

"You don't seem to be aware that the settlement calls for seven thousand dollars, not eighty acres of land. My client may have to accept the land in partial settlement, but in the process of foreclosure, she would no doubt receive a deficiency judgment against you and it would be up to you to find the cash to pay this judgment." The lawyer's words were crisp and cold.

Ben blinked. "How much would that amount to?"

"Well, we never know that until the foreclosure sale," Benton replied. Noting their consternation, he mellowed a little. "When the note becomes delinquent, we are obliged to begin foreclosure proceedings—and eventually the land is put up for sale. Someone might actually show up and bid the full seven thousand—which would satisfy my client and let you out. But that isn't likely to happen; so to protect Miss Bonner's claim, we would bid whatever lesser amount is necessary to repossess the property—say it would be four thousand. Then there would still be a judgment for three thousand against you—and, of course, in a way any property you own becomes security for such a claim."

"You mean we might be forced to sell some of our own land to pay the three thousand dollars?" Ben's voice could not conceal his distress.

"That's about the way it works," Benton answered.

"Well, what on earth can we do?" Betty asked in dismay.

"Oh, people manage to lick these problems every day, Mrs. Yeoman," Benton said complacently. "What I'd suggest is that you refinance this loan—I mean, borrow money elsewhere and pay off Miss Bonner. You'll probably have to pledge more security than the eighty acres, but I think it's the best way out."

A cold fear clutched at the hearts of Ben and Betty Yeoman as they left the lawyer's office. They were on the sidewalk, moving aimlessly, striving hard to think of what to do. Slowly they circled the town's three business blocks, and finally Ben said impulsively, "So it's money we need—then I guess the place to ask for it is here at the bank."

William Talbot, president of the town's national bank, was

a fleshy man with a somewhat pompous personality. He came
to this prairie village many years before to work as a book-
keeper in the dry-goods store. Then he married the banker's
daughter and became a bank teller, then cashier, and finally the
president. The indoor work had bleached his skin and kept
his hands soft and pink. The fringe of gray hair around his pale,
bald dome was always neatly cropped. He wore "Sunday
clothes" every day and never shed his coat in public no matter
how hot the temperature might be. Too fat, too soft and too
inept at physical undertakings to mow his own lawn, he was
nevertheless man enough to admire and respect the rugged,
hard-working men from the farms. Somehow he compre-
hended that his function in life was supplemental to theirs . . .
that it was their strong hands and tough vitality that translated
his knowledge and judgment into economic progress in the
community. A dozen times a day Talbot squirmed uncomfort-
ably in his sturdy oak swivel chair, vexed with the realization
that he was failing miserably in making this philosophy show
itself to the troubled, unhappy, discouraged customer seated
at the edge of his big oak desk.

When Ben and Betty Yeoman stated the purpose of their
call, Talbot got a folder out of his file and placed it on the desk.
He tapped the tips of his pink fingers together and said, "I told
Miss Bonner that this was bound to happen—that no farmers
hereabouts could afford such a price for land nowadays."

"I guess we've proved you were right," Ben observed.

"Now comes the question: What do we do next?" Talbot
went on. "I suppose you would like us to loan you seven thousand dollars."

"If it's agreeable," Ben said.

"I wouldn't recommend it, except under certain conditions,"
Talbot said coldly. Betty frowned and a flush of red tinted the

brown tone of Ben's weather-beaten face. "Your operations are too small, Ben. Even with this eighty along with your home place, you can't get ahead the way things are going nowadays."

"Then what do you suggest?" Ben asked nervously.

"Well," Talbot began, "maybe your problem can be solved by hooking it to another fellow's. You know the way young Jim Colton tried to set the world on fire after the war? He mortgaged the home place, bought a big spread of equipment, rented some more land, then bought some more at too high a price—till finally the whole show collapsed and the bank had to take the home place and the equipment. We could rent you the hundred-and-sixty-acre Colton place, Ben, and that along with the Bonner eighty would give you pretty close to five hundred acres for wheat. That's about right for one man to handle if he has good equipment and can hire some help to see him through the busiest periods."

Ben's eyes showed his surprise. "But I'd be stepping right into Jim's shoes . . . and if he couldn't make a go of it, why would I?"

"There's this difference, Ben. You're getting plenty of usable equipment at half its cost," Talbot replied.

"How much would this equipment cost us?" Ben asked. Talbot opened the folder and adjusted his glasses to read the figures on a small slip of paper.

"There's a big tractor with plows, harrow, drill, mower and combine. This stuff cost over seven thousand, but you can get it for three thousand dollars . . . at six per cent," he replied. "We'd require a mortgage on your crops as security for the six hundred dollars which you are to pay each year. Then we'd mortgage the machinery starting at twenty-four hundred and reducing it by six hundred dollars annually."

"But what about the Bonner place?" Ben asked.

"This may hurt," Talbot cautioned. "But here's how we feel about that. We'd carry this debt with a mortgage covering both the Bonner eighty and a hundred sixty acres of your homestead place—two forty in all. That would leave your quarter section with the buildings on it clear. We'd set the payments at five hundred a year and the interest at six per cent. You think it over and let me know this week."

"Great Scott!" Betty exclaimed when they left the banker. "We came to town expecting to shrink the farm by eighty acres and get ourselves out of debt, and now we're being bullied into adding one hundred sixty acres and going in debt—how much?"

"Ten thousand dollars," Ben answered in a faraway tone.

"That's an awful big debt, Ben," she said.

"It sure is, Honey. We've got a lot of figurin' to do; I can see that," Ben declared.

After supper, the Yeomans were busy with pencil and tablet. They figured what their plight might be if the Bonner settlement took an unfavorable course. They figured how they'd come out if they used the bank's terms only as they applied to refinancing the Bonner mortgage. And they figured the outlook using Talbot's complete plan.

"That fat dude!" Ben exclaimed. "He gets my goat. I'll bet that old fox has had this scheme in mind for days and has just been waiting for us to slide down the chute he's greased for us."

"But you've got to admit his plan looks the best," Betty observed.

"That's what gets me," Ben sputtered. "He doesn't look or act like he knew wheat from hazel brush, but he's no fool about farm arithmetic."

The Yeomans proceeded to do exactly as William Talbot advised, and the program started off very smoothly. Soon, however, bumps began to loom ahead. The secondhand combine broke down midway through Ben's harvest, and to save the rest of his crop, Ben had to hire it cut. The bill was $300. Then the price of wheat declined enough to shrink their income more than $400 below the figure expected. Just before Ben had screwed up his courage to go to the bank and explain his problems to Talbot, the good man had a stroke and died. The out-of-town banker who replaced him had an ice-cold disposition ... and when Ben came home from their meeting he brought Betty the gloomiest outlook they had ever known.

"The new banker will not back down a dime on the payment due on the machinery," Ben reported to Betty. "And we will not have enough left over from this year's crop to meet the mortgage payment and the interest."

"But doesn't he understand it was Mr. Talbot's plan?" Betty questioned.

"He seems to enjoy tearing up Talbot's propositions," Ben replied. "In fact, he said a bank had no business making farm loans except where there's proof that the farming is *very profitable*."

"But who needs to borrow money if they're making a big profit?" Betty exclaimed.

"Oh, the new banker says one should be making a good profit before he attempts to expand. So he loans money to successful people so they can be more successful—in a bigger way, that is," Ben explained.

"And we're not successful, so we don't deserve a loan," Betty said grimly.

"He sure made that plain to me," her husband stated. "He just as much as said we'd better start looking for money somewhere else."

"Where?" Betty's tone was dejected.

"There's a national farm loan office in town," Ben replied. "You know Dad shunned debt like it was poison, so we never learned much about the land bank system. Nobody on this farm ever dreamed of mortgaging it until we had to do it, Betty. I remember how Dad used to pity the neighbors who had land bank mortgages, but . . ."

It was an experience like a serious convalescence. Desperation drove the Yeomans to the farm loan association office to apply for a national farm loan; and then followed a round of check-ups (appraisals) that were as breath-taking as the diagnosis that tells you a critical operation is imminent, but the prospects of recovery are hopeful.

The Farm Loan Act of 1916 had provided for the establishment of the country's twelve Federal land banks for the purpose of making long-term loans—amortized over a period of thirty-three years—secured by first mortgages on farms. Interest rates were low—around 4 per cent. Most of the capital for starting these banks was appropriated by Congress, and the funds for the loans were obtained by sale of land bank bonds to investors. The long period of amortization in contrast to the five- to ten-year limits of the straight loans from banks and insurance companies considerably reduced the jeopardy of farmers using credit to finance their farming. The law, however, set the land bank loan limits at 50 per cent of the normal value of the land and 20 per cent of the value of the insured improvements. Within these limits, it was far from being an openhanded extension of easy credit for farm owners. Eventually, the system was supplemented by land bank commissioner loans (limited to $7500) through the Federal farm mortgage corporation, which permitted borrowing up to 75 per cent of a farm's prudent investment value.

Greatly to their dismay, Ben and Betty Yeoman learned that

the land bank's limit on a mortgage covering all of their land and buildings was $9250—$150 less than the outstanding balance of the loan William Talbot had arranged. To make up the difference, Ben sold a team for $90, his old tractor for $50, a calf for $12. With their finances reorganized, the Yeomans faced the future hopefully.

The year 1929 moved into its final months. Newspaper headlines in October blared the crash of the stock market and reported that Wall Street was in a panic. Of more concern to the Yeomans, however, was Carl's plan to get a white-collar job when he was graduated from State College the following June . . . and the departure of Sue and Meg to take nurses' training in a Portland hospital. Ben's fall wheat—240 acres of it—on his own land and the rented Colton place turned the fields a soft, rich green . . . and the winter's snows came and covered the land with a clean white blanket.

Sitting close to the cast-iron stove, her sewing basket in her lap, Betty reached for an apple in the hobnailed bowl on the drop-leaf walnut table. She split the apple with a paring knife, trimmed out a worm's path through the fruit and offered Ben a peeled section.

"You know, Ben, I sometimes wonder if we're really making any progress," she said.

"How so?" Ben asked.

"Well," Betty went on, "now we have twice as much land in wheat as Abner grew, but we're down to eating wormy apples—worse culls than your father fed to his pigs."

"I sometimes wonder about it myself," Ben replied.

Spring came to the prairie and Ben commenced his long rides back and forth across the gray surface of the fields that bore last year's wheat, guiding his big tractor in its tireless march across the land. Summer's first warm breezes swept over the moist furrows, and the fields became dry and dusty. Carl's letter came, telling of his graduation ceremonies and how he hoped his family could attend. Ben knelt low under the old Chevie's body and examined the tires . . . and Betty pushed the dresses back and forth along the rod in her clothes closet. At supper Ben said maybe they ought to sell the litter of spring pigs even if the best price lately had been only five dollars a head.

"We may as well face it, Ben," his wife responded. "We can't afford the trip to see him graduate. The pigs or anything else we could sell will not bring enough money to buy the clothes both of us need if we are to be presentable. And the tires and other probable expenses with the car are just beyond our means." Then she pretended to hear the cat meowing at the kitchen door and left hurriedly.

Carl spent a week end on the farm before he went to an army post to complete his military training and receive his commission as a second lieutenant in the Reserve Officer Training Corps. During his first two years at State College he was required to take basic military training; then he enrolled voluntarily for the two-year advanced course—partly because the small monthly pay received as army reserve trainee helped finance his college education and partly because he believed it was the obligation of a good citizen to use his opportunities to be well informed about the nation's military program. Training at the army post lasted six weeks, and then Carl returned to the farm to help his father with the combining.

Early in September, Sue came home for a week and there was a frantic scramble to get the house ready for her wedding. Ben gave his daughter in marriage to a young doctor Sue had met at the Portland hospital . . . and Betty fussed over the bridal couple's packing to see that space was made for a fruit box full of jams and jellies and pickles. The day after the wedding Carl left to take up his new position as instructor in vocational agriculture in one of the largest high schools in the state, and Meg went back to Portland to continue her training to become a graduate nurse. In the course of all these exciting and important events centering at the Yeoman homestead, Ben uneasily watched the price of wheat drop to fifty cents a bushel. After the young folks were gone, Ben scribbled a letter to the land bank explaining that if he sold his wheat at the present price he could not pay his loan installment and cover other bills, too. He was therefore holding his crop to sell at a higher figure and would make his payment to the bank as soon as this was accomplished. Betty copied the letter carefully in ink and it was deposited in their roadside mail box, on which the red metal flag was raised to signal the R.F.D. carrier that outgoing mail was waiting.

The bank's reply was stern and critical. The price of wheat did not advance and Ben remarked to Betty that the bank officials "ought to scold the price of wheat instead of the borrowers." But no matter who was to be scolded, the new year came and there was no improvement in the price. Harassed now by the dealers he owed for gasoline and repair parts, Ben sold wheat in small amounts to get enough money to appease his creditors temporarily and to keep the household supplied with bare essentials.

Came the harvest season for 1931 . . . then for 1932 . . . and the years were forming a pattern, a bleak, disheartening, cruel pattern. It was as if Ben and Betty Yeoman were not quite awake from the shock of a frightening nightmare. Time moved on, but there was no end to this bewildering trance. Debt— the icy horror of it—stalked them through the cold days of winter. Bills and expenses rose like a chilling fog and blotted the brightness out of every sunny day of spring. Pitifully low wheat prices became the blazing torches that added misery to summer's heat. Futility and hopelessness seeped into their spirits while the cold rains of autumn soaked the fields. The trance held on. The numbing fear of bankruptcy put its cold claws around their hearts. They toiled—grimly, desperately striving to break the spell that held them always just beyond the reach of the relief that would end this nightmare of despair.

A man who is master of things as powerful as the tractor and the combine . . . who can pilot this great mass of steel, this roaring commotion of energy, through a golden sea of his own fine, ripe grain . . . who can watch the miracle of the harvest and see the brown, gray earth yield a gushing, golden stream of man's most universal food . . . who can fill his bins and granaries with all this precious element—he must, indeed, grow sick inside to find it all so futile as now was happening on Ben Yeoman's land and on all the farms across this great nation. Here was the harvester pumping the rich blood of crops into the nation's economic arteries, yet no vitality resulted. Instead, the gushing flow of harvests lost their values, like the way red blood turns pale in the arteries of the anemic. Income—the lifeblood of farming—was suffering the plague of anemia.

And during the transition from earthbound agriculture to the agribusiness era, income anemia was one of the severest hardships the Yeomans encountered.

FOR HALF A CENTURY the significance of income on the farm had been growing rapidly. Back in the days when most of the population lived on farms, agriculture's production was largely consumed by the people who produced it. Only the smaller part left the farms for consumption elsewhere. This, however, was the part that provided income. So long as only a fraction of farm production would pay for purchased supplies, the ratio between cost and price was of minor importance. Taken as a whole, the farming population was relatively self-sufficient. Prices of farm products could range high or low and the effects on most of the farming people were neither extremely beneficial nor distressing. But when receipts from a major portion of farm output were required to pay for things the farm could not provide, then the relationship between cost and price gained importance. The tendency of mechanized agriculture to produce in excess of market demand coupled with the increased off-farm purchases created financial hardship, and subjected the farm economy to income anemia.

Of course, it was American farming's constantly expanding capacity to produce food and fiber for more and more people that made our tremendous industrial development possible. The day came when the population on farms ceased to increase—and then began to shrink—and still it succeeded in supplying the agricultural products needed by an ever-increasing number of people living and working in towns and cities. As fast as this transition progressed, the farming population became less and less self-sufficient and more and more dependent on income.

Had our progress been such as to make it possible to manipulate agriculture's production so that it was kept neatly in balance with consumption trends, there would never have been any serious problems concerning farm income. Unfortunately, agricultural production depends on factors the farmer cannot control—factors such as rainfall and sunshine, regularity of the seasons, fluctuations of temperature, flareups of pests and diseases. These mysterious whims of nature can make the harvests small or large.

But the big crop is by no means the blessing it might seem to be. Whenever the farms produce more of a product than the market has use for, its price drops. Although the produce may thus become a great "bargain" for the consumer, it rarely results in much of an increase in consumption because the demand for agricultural products is relatively inelastic. Usually each per cent of excess production takes its toll in a several times greater percentage reduction in price.

Depressed farm income is an old problem. It has spawned

numerous organized efforts to find solutions through legislation which, for many decades, has kept the government busy burning its fingers with farm programs. There was the Granger Movement in the 1870s, stimulated by the idea that high transportation costs and high prices for supplies were the main obstacles to profitable farming. The result was a great effort to organize farmers' purchasing associations and to influence legislation with respect to railroads and other transportation. Within the next twenty years, however, another factor was getting the blame for scanty farm profits: money was too scarce in the farming regions. The idea grew that the East, and Wall Street in particular, kept the supply of money corralled in the industrial centers. To lick this "conspiracy," farmers were strong for the Free Silver Movement and the Populist political activities. This pursuit of money finally shifted its direction and built up to the point where the government provided a fund to establish the Federal Land Bank System during World War I.

But even after fifty years of these efforts farm prosperity continued to be elusive. Just the same, there was always a new idea coming up—and this time it was from a man named Aaron Shapiro, who helped initiate farmers' marketing organizations in California. His apparent success caused great interest in his idea. It was simple enough—just organize practically all farmers in marketing co-operatives to which they were bound by ironclad contracts. All the milk, all the wheat, all the fruit, for instance, would thus be cornered by farmers' co-operatives and through the control over supply thus created, farmers could govern the prices to be paid for farm products. It was such a hopeful idea that it swept across the country in an amazing splurge of organizations. But making the idea work was something else. The temptation to reach for prices higher than were justified by the ratio of supply to demand was too great and the mere prospect that the scheme would raise prices tended to increase production much faster than markets could be developed. So the beautiful idea blew up like an overinflated bubble.

Next, farm hopes turned again to legislation, and the McNary-Haugen bills with their two-price grain-marketing plan based on equalization fees and export debentures were twice passed by Congress and twice vetoed by President Coolidge. But the pressure was increasing and when Herbert Hoover became President in 1929 he called a special session of Congress in April, and soon the Agricultural Marketing Act of 1929 was passed. This provided financing and assistance for setting up a new kind of nation-wide co-operative marketing corporations for major farm products such as grain, cotton and wool. Also, the Act of 1929 provided funds amounting to half a billion dollars—a breath-taking sum of money in those days—for the Federal Farm Board to use in assisting the marketing co-operatives and in stabilizing farm prices. Having been launched in an era of falling prices, the whole scheme had rough going. The big co-operative corporations that dealt in commodities having future contracts became snarled in a hassle for admittance to the future exchanges, and even the Farm Board's purchase of a grain firm in order to get a seat on the Chicago Board of Trade did not make for peace and harmony in the situation. One by one the national marketing units mired down in financial difficulties. Also, the direct stabilization efforts of the board resulted in heavy losses, and before long the Farm Board had the balance of its funds depleted or tied up in huge inventories of grain, cotton and wool. In spite of these great projects, prices continued to sag.

All this, however, was mere target practice prior to the big effort by government that came along with the Great Depression. In 1933, Congress passed the Agricultural Adjustment Act. It had a rather short life because it was declared unconstitutional in 1936. Then Congress redesigned its legislation, placing greater emphasis on conservation of soil and resources as a means to by-pass the unconstitutional features of the original act.

Ben Yeoman went to the courthouse and listened to the speakers tell about the Triple-A program. "What's it all about, Ben?" his wife asked him when he came home late that evening and slipped off his dress-up shoes, flexed his toes in their coarse Shaker socks, and settled to relax for a minute or two in the Morris chair.

"Well, it's the darnedest idea in some ways," Ben replied. "Seems we're to be paid *not* to grow wheat instead of to grow it."

"That is strange, isn't it?" Betty mused.

"Mostly, we've got too much of everything the farms produce. Good old Dad was always half afraid he wouldn't produce enough to live on—and now we're broke because we produce too much. And so are all the rest of the farmers, so I hear."

"But we have to produce a lot or we'd never meet our expenses," Betty remarked.

"That's the queer thing about it all," Ben muttered. "For years now, the county agent, the government bulletins, even a wise old banker like Talbot, have been telling us we must increase our efficiency. And how do we do that? Why we take on more land; we get implements that cultivate better and harvest with less waste; we speed up our work with tractors;

we switch to new varieties that yield better . . . and then we wake up and find we can't get a half or even a quarter of a decent price."

"So now Uncle Sam is going to pay us to quit being efficient —is that what you mean?" his wife asked.

"Well, not exactly that," Ben replied. "But if we do certain things like planting more alfalfa and less wheat, we get loans and payments from the government."

"In our case, Uncle Sam might as well not bother," Betty said ruefully. "We're way behind on our payments to the land bank, so I guess we owe him more money than he'll be paying us."

That was true. The Federal Land Bank started proceedings to foreclose on the Yeomans' mortgage. Vainly Ben and Betty searched for some way to borrow a few hundred dollars to stall off their bankruptcy, but these were times when every friend had the same problem: no money. In every gathering—on the streets, around the stoves in farmhouses, in the stores, in the repair shops—the conversation was full of gloom, full of words like "depression" and "foreclosure" and "sheriff's sale."

Then while the Yeomans were waiting for that ominous knock on the door, the knock of the grim, unhappy sheriff with a fateful paper in his hand, legislation was passed declaring there was a "debt moratorium" in behalf of those farmers who agreed to pay their creditors an amount approximating the rent which would have been due a landlord had they been renting their farm. Salvation though it was, Ben and Betty Yeoman found it by no means put an end to their troubled years.

The Triple-A payments paid for the seed that established alfalfa on the land they retired from wheat. And now they had so much hay to harvest that it became necessary for them to buy a baler ... and this, with other haying equipment, put them in debt to the dealer for the sum of a thousand dollars. During the worst years, the rent equivalent taken from their crops and paid to the land bank even fell short of paying the interest due under the terms of their loan, consequently increasing their total debt.

The hardships of 1934 were giving way to the hardships of 1935. Ben found his old combine unfit for another harvest, and in his search for some way out of this problem, he discovered that Chet Burns, a neighbor, was in a similar plight. Together they examined both machines and concluded they could use parts from one to make a usable harvester out of the other. Now that both farms had reduced their wheat acreage under the Triple-A program, the single rickety old combine could handle the crops on the two places.

"When combines first appeared around here, I told Ole' Johnson that neighbors ought to get together to own these expensive machines," Ben said to Chet while they tinkered with the repairs.

"You was only partly right," Chet said with a chuckle.

"How so?"

"You put a wrong word in there," Chet explained. "This machine ain't 'expensive'—worth, maybe, three hundred if we could catch a sucker." The two men laughed heartily.

One day a letter came from Carl. It said that he was married ... that he had a new job with the Soil Conservation Service ... that he was due to report in two weeks at the eastern office to which he was assigned ... that all these great and wonderful things had practically happened faster than he could describe them in his letter. His bride was Hilda Larson, the county agent's secretary—"the girl I told you I'd like to get serious about, Mom, if the darned Depression would just step aside and let a guy make some plans." Well, Carl and Hilda decided that the new and better job took care of their plans, and there was only time enough for a quick little wedding at Hilda's home and a combination honeymoon trip and journey to the new job in Carl's 1928 Model A roadster.

"Goodness sakes!" Betty exclaimed as she finished reading the letter to Ben and began inspecting the half-dozen snapshots Carl enclosed. One showed the Yeomans' tall, slender son with his arm around a dark-haired girl in a neatly tailored suit. "She looks sort of wholesome," Ben commented, "but I wouldn't say she was the prettiest girl I ever saw."

"Oh, how I wish we could have met her before it happened," Betty declared.

" 'Twould have been nice," Ben agreed. "But maybe they were sensible to take the plunge the way they did. If they'd waited to set up everything the way fathers and mothers would advise, they'd probably have lost their courage."

"If we can ever take a trip, Ben, we must go and visit the Larsons," Betty proposed.

"Yep," Ben responded. "It might be sort of lucky to be in-laws to a grocer's daughter."

"Mrs. Larson looks like a fine woman," Betty speculated as she studied the snapshots of her son's wedding party.

"Mrs. Larson had better say that about you, Honey, or I'll . . ."

And on another day a letter came from Meg with the news that she was going to be married to an ensign in Uncle Sam's Navy. The wedding was to be in San Francisco during his brief shore leave.

Away from the farm, life was offering at least some of the Yeoman family new vistas, romance, the prospect of new and hopeful outlooks. Although Ben and Betty Yeoman made their contacts with these pleasant and promising adventures through their mailbox, such letters did not come with sufficient frequency to offset the dread that again today the carrier would leave a packet of bills, delinquency notices and collection threats. Sometimes Ben would neglect to bring in the mail for two or three days, and Betty, knowing the game, would neither remind him nor go to the box herself. Playing it that way, there was always the chance that one of the cheerful letters from their son or daughters might arrive like an ace in a hand of cards and lift their spirits above the gloomy mood that the reminders of debt impose.

It had continued to be a Yeoman tradition for anyone writing to Carl to mention the 1927 Chevie as if it were a member of the family. Time was when the slightest scratch from a bush along the road was reported with anguish befitting a human accident such as a sprained ankle. Carl, in the full spirit of the game, usually closed his letters with the message, "Give my love to Chevie." Now it was 1940 and Chevie was thirteen years old. "You can tell the old gal that I'm jilting her for a jeep," this letter began ... and it was a breezy way for Carl to spring the news that he had been called from the Officers Reserve Corps to active duty as a captain in Uncle Sam's Army.

There was war in Europe and the price of wheat was rising ... rising just a little. On the strength of this outlook, Ben traded the old car for one of its several million sisters, one that started life in 1935 and admitted having traveled far enough to have wheeled her way twice around the earth's equator. Betty used the old tradition to begin a lighthearted letter to her son when the news came that his unit had been transferred to our nervous outpost in the Pacific—Honolulu. "Old Chevie almost died of a broken heart," Betty wrote, "but Dad said he couldn't tell for sure where her heartbreak would show up—

in the connecting rods, the transmission or the rear end. Anyway he couldn't stand to see her die around here so we took her to the matrimonial bureau (dealer's lot), where she can find herself a new lover. In her place, we brought home a sensible, spunky gal who is mature enough to be the sweetheart of a man with gray in his hair like your Dad has. I think the two of them have quite a case on each other, so your flirtations with the jeeps aren't likely to make her the least bit jealous."

Such banter put a gracious coating over the unpleasant circumstances the Yeomans were facing. Betty confided to her daughters, both of them graduate nurses, that she suspected she might be needing an operation but thought it best to wait until their finances were in better shape before she mentioned it to her husband. She promptly received special notes tucked inside the envelopes bearing the usual newsy letters she read aloud to Ben, and she smiled at the sensible precautions her daughters had taken by starting these notes with such words as "Tell that lady you mentioned to see her doctor *at once*. . . ." And there were times when Carl, too, delivered a scolding. "You haven't mentioned any hired help for a long time," he wrote. "Now listen to me! Dad is over sixty. Don't let him kid himself about being as husky as ever. . . ."

It had taken a well-aimed cross fire of lecturing from the whole family to prevail on Ben to spend the time and money to have his badly neglected teeth extracted and a set of plates made. "It'll be just my luck to have my false teeth fall out when I'm tinkering on the combine," Ben groused in his letters when at last he reported that the dental work was done. "And somebody's going to be sore when he takes a bite of bread that already has another man's teeth in it!"

"Better to lose them in a bale of hay," Carl bantered. "Some cow may be glad to get them."

The bantering came to a sudden halt. It was December 7, 1941. Japan attacked Pearl Harbor and among the casualties of that frightful catastrophe was Captain Carl Yeoman. Carl's wound necessitated the amputation of his left leg at a point a few inches above the knee. There followed many months of hospitalization, then the fitting for and training to use an artificial limb.

This tragedy was the toughest of all the blows that Ben Yeoman had taken. Tucked away in the back of his mind there had always been the thought that someday his son would join him on the farm and together they would make it prosperous and beautiful—once again, perhaps, the finest farm on the prairie, the same as it had seemed to be when Ben himself was the ambitious youth and Abner the respected, successful veteran. All these disheartening, dreary years between the birth of that dream and the time for its fulfillment had been bearable only because Ben kept on believing that all the hardships were merely temporary setbacks to the ultimate accomplishment. There were nights when he would wake in a cold sweat while his mind made terrifying calculations, toting up the years that had passed . . . the years that were left. Long ago he had ceased to say anything to Betty about this plan, this dream. And he knew that she needed no comment to assure her that it still remained the goal, their goal. He knew, also, that she understood his silence about it, knew that admission that the plan was frustrated by their poverty, their failures, was more painful to bear than all the hardships, discouragements and fruitless toil Ben endured.

Now the dream was dead.

That was the way Ben took the news. It came like the gong for the last round of a hopelessly one-sided fight for a boxer's championship belt. Not the sort to wilt and cringe and knuckle to defeat, certain though it is, Ben recoiled with all the savage desperation the disappointing years had planted in his heart. Like the mauled old boxer who gets up from the canvas without thought or feeling and throws his leather blindly, viciously, stubbornly all the way to the merciful knockout or the respite of the final bell, Ben drove hard at his labors. His temper raged against the whimsical moods of his equipment. The blue veins stood out in his neck as he bulled his strength against the weights to lift, the leverages to master. His face flushed dark red when the baler snarled its twine . . . when a motor was slow to respond to its starter . . . when the sun went down before he could finish the work he allotted himself for the day.

It was more than an old body could take. A neighbor driving past Ben's alfalfa field saw the tractor towing the baler in a zigzag line across the ground where baling had already been completed. He slowed his car and watched the tractor run crazily toward a pile of bales, bump against it and ricochet toward another. He stopped his car . . .

For Ben Yeoman, the troubled years had come to their end.

The hard and bitter life it had been Ben's lot to live was designed for him by the destiny of being at that certain place in that certain span of time which subjected him to the jeopardies that always exist where frontiers are new and their patterns unsettled. He was not a failure. He was an unfortunate man—unfortunate like the settler the Indians scalped on the outer fringes of our last earthbound frontier. Ben lived and struggled on the border between earthbound agriculture and the eruptive agribusiness era . . . enduring life's risks and hardships in the time and circumstances when the forces of the new era were running wild. Without his realizing that he had done so, Ben, too, had taken his place in the long line of Yeomans who pioneered on a new, raw, wild frontier.

The rawness, the newness of this frontier was exposed in many ways. Technology, for instance, was moving forward on an uneven front—a front as violent and inconsistent as was the way law and order moved across our land frontiers in its various forms ranging from private defense with a fast-drawn Colt to vigilantes, to posse and sheriff, to well-organized constabulary. Research in agriculture proceeded piecemeal, but with its emphasis on production. As a result, the productive capacity of farms rapidly outgrew the markets for farm products. Long before research's contribution to increased production could be more than partially utilized we were suffering the penalties of overproduction. We had won the biggest of the agricultural battles, but we were losing the whole war, the conquest of agribusiness, for lack of complementary research to find markets and uses for the vast production we had made our farms capable of producing.

Exposed on this new frontier, too, were the dangerous failures in co-ordinating the actions of the main body with those of the outposts. In terms of frontier warfare, it made a situation such as the caravans of covered wagons faced when hostile Indians cut off those which were too far ahead or too far behind. We suffered losses because we were neglecting to look after the whole of agribusiness and instead attempted to meet its problems only where we thought they existed in the farming segment. Consequently we were caught deep in new, strange territory without having the wisdom to unite all parts of agribusiness in an attack on its problems. Farm leaders, businessmen and public officials continued to seek answers to the farm problem, oblivious of its transposition into an agribusiness problem

—a problem that challenged the co-ordinated brains of the leaders of agriculture and its related businesses and sciences. In making our agricultural progress, we had helped Ben Yeoman and countless others like him venture deep into the new frontier of agribusiness, there to let them flounder and suffer because the organization of the new frontier's resources was too immature to provide the needed supporting elements: the interlocking forces of agriculture and its related businesses. Ben was one of the pioneers trapped in the violence of an untamed frontier.

The tragic part about a life hammered by hardships endured in seemingly futile conflict with overpowering forces is that all this punishment can occur right in the midst of the resources that may someday provide comfort and prosperity. Ben Yeoman's overwhelming problems dealt with income and capital. What is it that puts income and capital at the service of mankind? Most of all, it's the strength developed within each segment of the economy—strength to counteract the constant pressures that squeeze enterprises between rising costs and falling prices. When farm and business leaders succeed in developing such strength in the agribusiness segments of the economy, the hardships of the new frontier will begin to give way to successes and satisfactions.

Part Three

THE AGRIBUSINESS ERA

Parts of the substance of the thing we call agribusiness have existed for a long, long time. Now, however, there is evidence that we have come to a period in which the businesses we include in the agribusiness segment of the economy seem bound to expand and multiply. This can and will go on whether or not it goes by the name of agribusiness. Technological progress and economic forces are in motion and we are in an era that will see them creating many changes with respect to everything that agriculture can produce. If so much has already happened, and so much more is inevitable, what then is important about the agribusiness idea? Its importance is the challenge to think and plan and act so that we use to the fullest advantage the big framework of the agribusiness idea. We are challenged to understand the agribusiness idea . . . to apply it wherever and whenever we have or can make the opportunity . . . to use it to create new methods of farming, new products, new services, new businesses that lead to greater economic progress.

9.

THE TRANSITION from earthbound agriculture to agribusiness exposed the challenge facing those of us who seek opportunity on this new frontier. The challenge is to develop a good way of life for agribusiness people ... to enable them to keep in step with the progress of other segments of our economy ... to help them contribute greatly to the total prosperity of the American people.

The challenge demands both individual and united effort to meet it. We are still on a frontier, and many of us will be pioneering in the agribusiness area for a long time to come. Always it is up to the pioneer to be resourceful, adaptable, self-reliant. Those are standards the individual must attain. But without uniting his efforts with others and thus co-ordinating and compounding their multiple achievements, no lasting development can be accomplished. Agribusiness can provide a good way of life only as the individuals engaged in it unite in recognizing the standards it demands of them and then work together to prepare themselves to measure up to these standards. What these standards are to be and how we are to approach them are things we must learn from a great accumulation of experience, a great deal of planning, a very determined effort to integrate our diverse interests throughout the scope of agribusiness. Together we must learn what *par* should be in each and every agribusiness category . . . and what *par* should be for the individual's part in each respective category.

The transition from earthbound agriculture to agribusiness was particularly rough because we advanced along a ragged, uneven front. The parts of our advance that ran way out ahead of the rest seemed to be making spectacular progress. We mass-produced many things that made farming more efficient and more productive—sometimes altogether too productive—and each thing we accomplished in making this progress seemed of itself to be a very praiseworthy and fortunate achievement. But it was this harum-scarum progress that occasionally devastated agriculture and now gives us reason to plan the development of the agribusiness frontier with a great deal more attention to co-ordination of its units. In effect, we entered this new frontier like a cavalcade of covered wagons crossing dry country and coming in sight of a watering place, whereupon some wagons break out of the column and race ahead pell-mell, only to find they are running right into an ambush of hostile Indians.

To carry this analogy a little further, it was the inability of farming to balance its production with the demands of its markets that put the agricultural wagon in the headlong rush into an economic ambush where it was at the mercy of conditions which provided insufficient income for farming. And for twenty years following World War I, capital erosion, low income, poverty, debt and hardship harassed farming like an Apache war party circling round and round a stranded settler's wagon. No real rescue was forthcoming until World War II came along and created sufficient increase in the demand for farm products to cause them to rise in price . . . and when that happened the marauders ceased their attack and the wagon moved peacefully on toward the watering place.

Like the pioneer's widow who survived the attack of the savages and then experienced that strange, quiet calm that comes with exhaustion from the fury and desperation of the struggle, Betty Yeoman began making the adjustments that life required. Ben's will left her with title to most of the farm, while Carl, Sue and Meg received a portion of the acreage in joint tenancy. There was no alternative but to relinquish the lease on the Colton place; so now the farm's operations were thus reduced to Abner's homestead acreage plus the eighty acres of the Bonner purchase. Little by little the pattern of a new outlook began to form.

"David, how many pancakes can you eat this morning?" Betty asked her small grandson as he watched wide-eyed while she stirred the batter. The old farmhouse kitchen had come alive again—a place where a child's questions probed for an explanation of every domestic incident . . . a place where the family previewed each day's outlook.

"O-o-oh 'bout six," David calculated.

"My goodness!" Betty exclaimed. "Why so many?"

"That's one for each year old I am," David replied.

"It's pretty nice to be six, isn't it, David?"

"But I'd like to be older than that," the boy declared.

"Why do you want to grow up so fast?"

"So I can run a farm," he answered. "Six is no good for that. I want a pony ... yes, and a pig ... and maybe some chickens. But my mommy and daddy always say, 'Now, David, you be patient. You're too young yet to take care of animals.' You know, Gran'-mother, we almost had a dog once."

"What do you mean, 'almost'?"

"Well, this was on the army post ... and this dog came along. He was black and he had woolly ears. He came right in the house and he was awful friendly. But, you know something? He was everybody's dog. My daddy said he was an army tramp. Well, he just stayed for a while. But he was almost ours." The boy slid into one of the chairs at the breakfast table.

"That was your great-grandfather's place," Betty said. "I think it would be nice if you would use it now."

"Do I look like Great-Grandfather?" David asked.

Betty chuckled. "His hair was dark like your mother's—and your hair is red. Wonder where you got that red hair."

The boy looked at her skeptically. "Was your hair red once?"

"Goodness sakes, David! I forgot. It's almost white now. But when I was a little girl, my hair was red, just like yours."

"Was Grandfather's hair ever red?" the boy asked.

"No, David, for a long time it was dark, almost black ... then it began to turn gray. Say, boy, you'd better call your folks for breakfast. ... Here, take this old sheep bell and ring it in the hall."

Hilda Yeoman intercepted her son in the sitting room. "What's this? Mess call?" she asked, raising her voice above the bell's clanging.

"You don't say 'mess' on a farm," David said scornfully.

"This is a sheep's bell and Grandmother said it's for calling folks to meals."

Entering the kitchen, Hilda spoke cheerily. "You're spoiling me, Betty. . . . I should have rolled out and taken my little Indian in charge instead of letting him riot all over the place."

Betty laughed. "Waking early is just an old habit . . . and Davy's company was very welcome."

"Carl's on his way," Hilda said. "Shall I pour the coffee?"

Carl Yeoman, now thirty-four, was back in the kitchen of his boyhood. The pine chunks burning in the black iron range, the bacon and the coffee gave the room the same pleasant smells he remembered from his boyhood. "A kiss for the cooks!" he exclaimed as he stepped between his wife and his mother and, swinging an arm around each, squeezed them close.

"What are you going to do in those clothes?" David asked, a scornful look clouding his boyish face as he ran his eyes over the bleached old army fatigue clothes his father was wearing.

"Oh, these?" Carl parried. "Well, I figured we would all take a good walk around the farm, and these are the best kind of clothes for that."

"But Mom's got on her good clothes," David countered. "Don't you have any sloppy clothes, too, Mommy?"

"Davy-boy, this is just an old gabardine skirt—and look at my feet . . . my old loafers and a pair of old golf socks. Isn't that sloppy enough, Davy?"

The boy nodded, but he seemed preoccupied. Somewhat shyly he sidled close to his grandmother and, giving her apron a gentle tug, he looked up to her eyes and solemnly asked, "Grandmother, would you put on your cow-woman dress when we go for the walk?" Betty's jaw dropped in surprise, but as she smiled the little wrinkles spread from the corners of her eyes and flickered playfully at her temples.

137

"Davy, what on earth are you talking about?" Hilda exclaimed.

"In the movies, the people wear cow clothes on farms, don't they?" the boy challenged. "I used to have a cowboy suit to wear, you said, when we'd visit the farm. But it got too small. You do have a cow-woman dress, don't you, Gran'-mother?"

Betty struggled to suppress an outburst of laughter. "Davy-boy, you're thinking of the big cattle ranches. This is just a farm. Mostly we just wear what we call work clothes—and sometimes I think they would fit cows better than people," she said with a chuckle. "Here now, let's sit down to breakfast. Davy's sitting in his great-grandfather's chair."

"The fourth generation of the Yeoman family to sit there," Carl remarked, a note of awe in his voice. "The Yeoman man who sits there asks the blessing, remember, Davy?" They sat down and the little boy bowed his head and said, "We thank thee, Lord, for this food, for our blessings . . . and bless the memory of Abner Yeoman, my great-grandfather, and Benjamin Yeoman, my grandfather. Amen." Betty pressed her fingers to her eyes, then smiled at David and said, "That was very fine, and it made me very proud of you."

"Mom said you'd sure like it," David replied with utter candor. Hilda blushed crimson, but she was relieved to feel the gentle pressure of Betty's fingers on her wrist, a gesture hidden beneath the table cover.

The artificial leg gave Carl a jerky gait, but he moved with a deliberate air, like a man who plainly meant that wherever he was going he was on his way with determination echoing from every step. He was lean and tall, and the weeks of lounging on sunny hospital balconies had tanned him brown as logging camp coffee. He led the way to Abner's orchard, going straight to the tree that bore the sweet, white-fleshed summer peaches. Half the limbs were dead and bare, and pits beneath the tree showed that birds had consumed the few fruits the season had provided. He tried to tell his son about the bigness, the beauty and the generosity of this tree as he remembered it when he was a boy, but David's expression registered no perception of the boyhood wonderland he was attempting to portray. It was a scraggy, ugly old tree . . . that was the only way David could ever remember it.

They passed through the orchard. Carl looked back. The trees were bushy, neglected. Weeds grew tall around the tree trunks. Sick, insect-riddled, immature fruit littered the ground beneath the limbs.

"When you get a few spare dollars, Mom," Carl said, "I think you ought to hire a bulldozer and clean out most of these old trees. You could clear about ten acres for wheat or alfalfa."

"I suppose it's what ought to be done," his mother replied, "but I do hate to see what used to be your grandfather's pride disappear entirely. It gave us so many good things to eat. Remember?"

"I sure do," the young man answered.

They walked around the old log shed where the forsaken header cowered under a heap of wreckage. "As soon as snow falls, I'm coming out and put a match to that junk pile," Carl said.

His mother stepped up on a section of the tumble-down roof of the shed. She put her left hand over her eyes and, turning slowly, pointed her right forefinger at faraway places on the prairie.

"What are you doing, Mom?" Carl asked.

"I'm counting abandoned farmsteads, Son. Would you believe it? There are twelve old homesteads, empty or gone," she answered.

"It takes a bigger farm to provide a living nowadays," Carl observed. "Granddad's was a big operation in his day—but, gosh, four or five places like his would be just a nice size to-day." He noticed his mother's frown and quickly changed the subject.

"I miss the livestock," Carl stated, "but I guess it's just as well there's none requiring daily chores now."

David spoke up suddenly. "I thought you had some pigs here on the farm, Daddy," he challenged.

"That was a long time ago," Hilda explained.

The boy scuffed his shoe in the dry earth. "Is there something kinda dopey 'bout this farm now?" he asked in a voice of genuine concern.

Carl coughed nervously, and Hilda said with casual reassurance, "David, things get old on farms and they wear out or need to be changed. . . . It's the same as with little boys' cowboy suits. Don't you see?"

In the days that followed, the feeling of defeat, of merciless uncertainty, gradually lifted from Betty's spirits. Carl's experience with paper work—as a vocational teacher, a soil conservation agent and in the army—enabled him to analyze and classify the farm's circumstances. Hilda, too, was exceedingly helpful. Using the old portable typewriter that had shared Carl's career through college and his later activities, she deftly prepared page after page of records and plans that Carl assembled in a loose-leaf notebook which he named "the brain."

"For the first time in all my life I'm beginning to understand our problems," Betty said as she listened to Carl's explanation of the pages in "the brain."

"You and Dad kept a pretty good set of records," Carl commented. "Otherwise we'd have a rather empty 'brain'—one that wouldn't be much help in making any plans." The plan that evolved was for Betty to rent the farm, reserving the farmstead area—the house, barn and outbuildings—for her residence. The rental would be a share of the crops—one third of the wheat and half of the alfalfa hay. Out of the proceeds from the sale of the landlord's share of these, the farm's taxes, mortgage payments, and operating upkeep would be paid. Disposition of the remaining income was to be budgeted each year according to the family's agreement, the first consideration, of course, being to provide a satisfactory living for Betty. Beyond that, if money was available, improvements would be made, or more of the mortgage paid off, or the day might come when there would be enough cash to permit distributing some of the farm's income to Carl and his sisters.

"I know that the way things are working out, something you and Dad had always hoped would happen seems to be fading out of the picture," Carl said as he stood behind his mother, who was seated at Abner's old writing table looking thoughtfully at the open pages of "the brain." "It was your dream, I know, for me to come back to the farm someday—perhaps going into partnership with Dad—but at least being ready to carry on the family traditions right here when the time came."

Betty said, "Yes, Carl, we had such a dream—but I believe both your dad and I knew long ago that the dream was one thing and reality was something else. You see, when we were young, farming here was such an enviable way to live. I can remember the way the merchants, our friends in town—and especially the old family doctor—used to speak with such admiration of your grandfather. He was 'big success' around here, and everybody made it plain to me—in a nice way, of course—that I was a lucky little redhead to get in on such a prosperous situation. But I'm grateful to fate that Hilda and you were spared the hardships of life here on the farm at the time you were married. As time went on, I think one of the great unspoken fears that haunted your dad and me was that you might be trapped by circumstances and forced to come back here . . . to a situation that was anything but enviable."

"A high-school teacher isn't what you'd call royally paid," Carl remarked. "But even so, I was able to make much more than you and Dad were making here during those same years. And now it would take at least three farms like this to make as much as my pay as a captain in the army. For a guy with two good legs, it would still be tempting to try to get a footing on a big enough farm . . . even if the going promised to be rough for quite a while." Then he laughed. "We Yeomans have always been just a little crazy, Mom."

"I know what you mean, Son," Betty said softly.

The visitor drove a black pickup truck. He got out slowly, paused to look around respectfully, then tapped his pipe on the heel of his stockman's boot to loosen the ashes that he carefully ground into the earth. The man was elderly, lean and bronzed. He wore a cloth hat that matched the material of his zipper jacket and trousers, a greenish gabardine. David abandoned his game of torpedoing a toy battleship on the back porch and rushed to the dooryard gate to greet the stranger.

"Are you a cattle rancher?" the boy asked.

The old man chuckled. "No, Sonny," he answered. "I'm just an old sodbuster."

"What's a sodbuster, sir?" David inquired respectfully.

"Well, Sonny, he's just a plain farmer—one who plows, harrows and harvests," the man explained. "I guess you must be Carl Yeoman's boy. Is your daddy home?"

Betty appeared at the farmhouse door. "Hello, Jim," she greeted. "I see you're getting acquainted with my grandson. Mr. Brown, this is David—Carl's little boy. Do come in, Jim."

"Fine boy . . . make a good farmer, too," the visitor commented. "Just thought I'd come over and maybe chat some with Carl while he's home."

Jim Brown's chat turned out to be quite a surprise. The elderly neighbor was one of the prairie's ablest farmers as well as one of its most successful businessmen—largest stockholder of the Prairie Farm Supply Company. The problem on Jim Brown's mind was that Uncle Sam had sent his greetings to the young manager of the supply company, and he was due to report for military service within two weeks. The wartime demand for man power being now at its height, finding a capable replacement was no easy task.

"I figured it might be something you'd like to do," Jim said to Carl. "You've certainly had a lot of good background for such a job . . . and it would keep you here on the prairie. Dare say that would make Betty kinda happy, too."

"This is something I'd never thought about," Carl said, hedging. "There were some things to do here to help Mother handle the farm's problems, and after that I expected to find a job in a war plant. I've got a score to settle with our enemies, you know, and it's personal as well as patriotic."

"That I can understand," Brown said. "But this job would put you back in the fight, remember. Movin' food up to the front, so they tell me, is just as necessary as movin' ammunition up to the guns. It's all gotta start somewhere—and doin' the movin' up at the back end of the line is just as important as 'tis at the front end. You help us keep our supply line to the farms a-workin' the best way possible and you'll be doin' a big man's share of the stuff it takes to fight a war and win it."

The Prairie Farm Supply Company was quartered in an old freight house on a siding near the town's railroad station. There was a platform along one end from which farmers' trucks could load supplies. A small room in one corner of the building served as an office, and the rest of the space was filled with stacks of feed, fertilizer and seed, bales of twine for binders and hay balers, spools of barbed wire and rolls of fencing and asphalt roofing, cases of tonics, disinfectants, chemicals and medicines, and racks containing repair parts, hardware and accessories for farm machines. Outside, the space between the freight house and the street was cluttered with old and new farm machinery, hog feeders, water tanks and fuel drums.

"Sort of like an army depot," Jim Brown commented, hoping to capitalize on Carl's military interests.

"Yes and no," Carl responded. "Depending on whether you mean before or after a raid."

Jim Brown looked crestfallen.

"Never mind that crack," Carl said. "I'll take the job. I'll pass the ammunition through here like . . ."

The elderly man's face crinkled in a broad grin. "We'll sure be grateful to you," he said.

On the outskirts of town, Carl and Hilda found a little, old house that they could rent. Back of the house there was a small barn dating from the days of the horse and buggy, but now it served as a garage and woodshed, with space left over for storage or other purposes. The old barnyard behind the buildings was surrounded by a picket fence adorned with red rambler roses that bloomed profusely and gave the rather shabby property a touch of elegance. There was good soil for a garden both inside the barnyard and between its fence and the house. Thrifty former residents of the property had set out everbearing strawberries, raspberries, asparagus and rhubarb along the walkway to the barn, and the last tenant had planted a variety of vegetables and taken such good care of them that Hilda found there were now snap beans, carrots and beets ready for their table and for canning.

The news about Carl's new job and his renting a house in town spread rapidly in the community, and soon Betty was receiving calls from neighbors who wanted to rent the farm. Carl made out a check list of the things to consider in selecting a renter—items such as the applicant's equipment, the size of his other operations, the quality of his farming and how progressive he seemed to be. He made the rounds of the prospective renters' farms and sized them up, carefully recording his observations in his pocket notebook as soon as he had driven out of sight of their places.

"But we know some of these people so well," Betty protested. "I don't think you need to fuss with so many details. Now take the Whites—they're honest and hard-working . . ."

"Yes, Mother," her son answered. "But they have only one old tractor—and more work than it can do now and do it right."

Soon Carl was very glad he undertook his methodic checkup. It became evident that his mother was easily swayed by sympathy for the not-so-successful neighbors, or she might base her selection on a long-standing friendship that completely disregarded the prospect's capabilities. Rather than be trapped in debates as to which was more important, a good set of field equipment or the loan of four spools of twine several seasons back when Ben used all he had and was too short of cash or credit to buy enough more to finish his crop, Carl resorted to chart techniques he had used in the classroom and in his soil-conservation work. He gave each applicant a number and put these numbers across the top of his chart. Down the left side of the chart he listed the factors to be considered. Under the applicant's number he wrote a rating for each of these factors. When the chart was completed, he explained it to his mother.

"Now you can see Number Six is by far the best, can't you, Mother?"

"Well, you say he has the best tractors and scores good on other machines," Betty said, hedging.

"And he controls erosion better than any of the others. Rates high on yields. Uses new ideas. Now do you agree he's top man?" Carl pressed.

"Maybe, though, he doesn't need more land," his mother said, wavering.

"Mother!" Carl said sternly. "The problem before us is to manage this farm successfully. Unless it's a success it's not going to help anybody, is it? So, first, let's use our heads and put it in hands that are most likely to operate it right. If it's well managed, it'll be an asset to the whole community—yes, and to us and to the renter. But if it's poorly managed, what happens? The community gets a run-down farm; a renter takes on more than he can handle and suffers accordingly; and you'll be worrying about the mortgage and the taxes."

"So you want me to agree to your Number Six?" Betty parried.

"At least I want you to recognize the strong points in his favor, see," Carl cautioned. "I want you to realize that there are good reasons to rent the farm to him regardless of who he is. That's because it may turn out that his wife peeves you because she monopolizes the party telephone line ... or you have some objection like that."

"Oh, don't be silly," Betty scoffed. "I'll take the medicine even if it's bitter. Who's your Number Six?"

Carl, though he knew the answer, went through the ceremony of referring to his code before speaking the name— "Chester Burns."

"For pity sakes!" Betty exclaimed. "Chet was a great buddy of your dad's, even though he was years younger than your father. Well, I'm pleased and satisfied."

The next problem was to find someone who would live on the farm and share the big house with Betty—someone who would fit neatly into a situation where every piece of furniture, every pot and dish, every picture on the walls, had settled into a pattern reflecting Betty's lifelong tastes and habits. Carl and Hilda knew that they were welcome to make the farm their home, and although they had not talked about it, each sensed that the other secretly believed that to do so would be an admission that they would be losing some of their own brave, self-reliant outlook toward life if they accepted this convenient shelter. It was something that Betty, too, understood and she gracefully avoided drawing them out about it. When Carl was offered the job in town, the wartime rationing of gasoline provided a reason for making other plans. Now, Carl said, it just wouldn't be patriotic to apply for enough gas for the long daily drive to town and back if it were possible to reside in town.

It was Hilda who worked out the plan that answered Betty's need for companionship. Being the wife of an army officer had acquainted Hilda with the problems that arise when the man of the house leaves for military duty in some faraway place.

147

So she quietly set about checking on the families of men called to the armed services. Most of them turned out to be young wives who moved in with their parents, but finally Hilda's quest led her to the family of Dr. John Turner, the younger of the town's two dentists. Dr. Turner was nearly forty and neither he nor his wife had any close relatives. When Dr. Turner volunteered his services to the navy, there was no family home to receive his wife and children. The Turners had two sons, Bobby, nine and Henry, eleven, and their home was a rented apartment—an expensive and not very spacious environment for two boisterous youngsters. Nancy Turner was a Cub Scout den mother, and Hilda used David's interest in joining the Scouts as a reason to cultivate acquaintance with the dentist's wife.

Hilda discovered that Nancy Turner had two interests that were particularly compatible with the program she was seeking to develop. One was that Nancy loved outdoor life.

"If I had my way, we'd buy or rent a place like the one you have," she told Hilda, "but John is city-bred and he insists that dude farming, as he calls it, would be a silly thing for us to try."

Nancy's other interest was writing short stories.

"I collect rejection slips," she said with modesty, "and console myself that it's the bedlam around here that keeps me from writing anything good enough to deserve a check from a magazine. I do get at it for a quiet hour in the morning now and then while the boys are at school, but when they're around here I'm on pins and needles . . . wondering if a ball is going to break a neighbor's window . . . or I'll look out and see them wrestling in that pretty flower garden next door."

"I take it you'd just as soon live where there's more room," Hilda ventured.

"Indeed I would," Nancy replied. "Especially if it gave me a quiet place to do my writing."

When Hilda discussed her plan with Betty she was surprised to find her mother-in-law had already begun to make adjustments in her home that prepared the way for such a program.

"I decided it was foolish for me to have my personal things spread all over this big house," Betty said, "so I did some rearranging to concentrate them in Abner's den and the room next to it. You see, Ben's father was a man who had a place for everything and everything in its place. All the records and the most prized pioneer relics are fitted into the built-in shelves and racks of his den. It makes a cozy, private sitting room for me . . . and I can use the bedroom next to it. Well, the rest of the house could be a country club for all that it need bother me."

"Then you think it would be all right to make Mrs. Turner a proposition?" Hilda questioned.

"My dear girl," Betty responded, "I think it's a wonderful idea. If it appeals to her and will benefit those two boys while their daddy's off to war, then I'll be very pleased."

For the young Turners, summer on the farm was the grandest time of their lives. All too soon the hot days of August gave way to September's temperate weather . . . and then the school bus was picking them up at the farm lane at a quarter to eight in the morning and dropping them off at a quarter past four in the afternoon. Sometimes on Fridays Davy Yeoman joined them on the homeward trip and spent Saturday and Sunday at the farm, much to the delight of his grandmother.

Captain Carl Yeoman's command of the Prairie Farm Supply Company was beginning to impress the community. He had been on the job less than two weeks when suddenly the entire

149

establishment was transformed from a seedy, run-down clutter of machines and materials to a neatly organized, clean,
dressed-up array of merchandise. Carl accomplished this by
carefully planning an efficient rearrangement of the inventory;
then he employed the entire vocational agriculture class from
the high school for eight hours' work on a Saturday. Using
his military training, Carl assigned the boys to work units according to their professed preferences and his estimates of their
abilities. Then he briefed each group on its assignment and
designated a leader to guide the progress and to contact him
in case any question arose as to how to proceed. There were
thirty-three boys in six groups and it took an hour for Carl
to get them organized. But when all were ready, Carl gave the
signal and for a little while the place looked as if it were an
island where the Marines were landing in the Pacific conflict.
Another hour, and the jumble began to show signs of transformation to orderly arrangement. Two hours more, and the
dingy freight house wore a new coat of brown paint, the dark
and gloomy office had expanded into a spacious salesroom enclosed by plywood walls bearing a cedar stain, the disheveled
stockroom was groomed to display orderly stacks and piles
of merchandise bounded by wide, straight stripes of yellow
painted on the warehouse floor. Outside, the machinery collection was lined up like artillery ready for regimental inspection. Crushed gravel was spread on passageways between the
equipment, and a bright new roadside sign was set at the street
corner proclaiming the Prairie Farm Supply Company was
ready to serve the community. Hilda, helped by Nancy, Betty
and two of the mothers of the high-school boys, arrived at five
o'clock with picnic baskets bulging with potato salad, pickles,
cakes and cookies. Carl and his KP group set up a cinder-block

grill and started hot dogs roasting. Soon as the eats were gone, Carl handed each boy three crisp one-dollar bills.

"Gosh, Mr. Yeoman," the class president exclaimed, "we had so much fun it doesn't seem right to take the money."

"Never mind. You earned it," Carl replied, "but if you liked being here, just go around and tell folks that Prairie Farm Supply Company is ready to serve every farm—like our new sign says."

Jim Brown arrived early the following Monday. Carl showed him around, and while they were inspecting the transformation, two customers entered the salesroom. One let out a low, long whistle and said to the other, "Say, that one-legged captain sure goes for the spit-and-polish, doesn't he?"

Jim grinned and nudged Carl in the ribs. "He means we're darn proud of the way you do things," Brown declared.

There was more to distributing supplies to farms than spit-and-polish at headquarters, Carl soon became aware. Corregidor had surrendered, the Japs were swarming down the Malay Peninsula, Hitler's Panzer divisions were ripping France to shreds . . . and orders for rubber tires, barbed wire, nails, burlap and grease suddenly floundered in a quagmire of wartime regulations . . . allocations, priorities, rationed quantities.

The price of wheat rose above the dollar mark, and farmers prepared to rip up sods and seed more grain to supply the fighting forces and war-stricken populations of the Allied Nations. On the prairie, the sudden conversion of alfalfa fields to wheat produced a clamor for barbed wire to fence off the areas now newly seeded to wheat and no longer available for cattle pasture after hay crops were harvested. Carl watched his company's stock pile of spools of barbed wire melt away while he scouted desperately for replacement stocks.

"I can get an allotment of a little more than half a carload from the East," he reported to Jim Brown, "but the manufacturer can't ship less than a carload. Do you think we can find some other distributor around here who can qualify for the rest of a carload?"

"Well," Jim replied, "there's the Johnson Brothers—our strongest competition. But Old Ole won't like the idea. Maybe you remember the Johnsons—they used to operate the threshin' machines with the big steam engines. Always held to the idea that being completely independent is shrewd, smart business. That philosophy has made Ole a hustler . . . and plenty prosperous. Don't think he'll go for your idea, but you can try."

Carl went to see the Johnsons. Their place of business was on the south end of Main Street, where they operated a gas station and a public scale to weigh hay and livestock outbound from the prairie's farms. Between the scale house and the gas pumps they had installed a big salesroom with wide plate-glass windows, and back of this was a repair shop to service tractors and trucks. The Johnsons, to say the least, were all-rounders when it came to country-town business enterprises. Ole, who managed the establishment, was a fat old man, bald and gray. Carl found him sitting on a bale of hay in the scale house. Ole's "mornin'" was a cool and definitely reserved greeting, Carl noticed.

After a brief warm-up of small talk, Carl explained the object of his visit. "You see, Ole, my company's quota isn't enough for a carload of wire—and probably your company is in the same situation. So if we get at this problem together, I think we can qualify for a carload shipment. That will help a lot of farmers if we can do it."

"Too much red tape—'tain't worth while," Ole declared.

"Oh, it's going to involve some paper work," Carl admitted, "but that won't kill us."

Ole's frown was grim. "I don't much go for this 'us' stuff," he said. "Johnson Brothers have their own way of doing things."

"Sure, Ole, but here's a chance to do a good turn for every farmer who needs wire."

"We don't want anybody sayin' Johnsons are so eager to make an extra buck that they're willin' to tangle themselves in any old scheme to do it."

"But suppose a lot of farmers lose money because it hurts the Johnsons' pride to quit being so independent?"

The ponderous man bristled and rocked his great bulk nervously on the bale of hay.

"So for running my business my own way, I'm a devil wearing horns! How do I know this 'us' scheme of yours ain't just a plan to horn in on Johnsons' business?"

"You're not afraid of competition, I dare say," Carl cut in.

Ole spat his tobacco juice into the heap of hay fragments that had drifted into a corner.

"Take this business of yours, Ole. Do you know what you're really trying to do with it?"

Ole scowled. "Of course I know. I'm trying to figure out what it is that's going to be needed, then have it ready, and when the customers come for it, I'll make a few bucks. Enough to live on, I hope."

"I think what you and I are trying to do, Ole, is have a hand in running every farm in the county."

"What do you mean, running farms? Let 'em run their own confounded farms, and leave me run *my* business," Ole fumed.

"A farm's a business, too, Ole. It buys something, produces something, sells something. In my granddad's day, farms bought very little. Look at that hay scale, for instance—there's where hay goes out of here to buy the gas and tractors you sell next door. Not so long ago the hay stayed on the farms and there wasn't a gas pump in town. What happened? Suppliers like you and me set up to act as purchasing departments of the farms around here. We help run these farms, don't we?"

"You're talkin' pretty fancy," Ole said disdainfully.

"No, I'm serious about it," Carl declared. "You said, Ole, that you tried to figure out what would be needed—well, doesn't that mean you're trying to help your customers keep their operations going? Seems to me you're trying to help them run their farms."

"I'm runnin' my business—my brother's and mine," Ole muttered.

"Sure you are. But you're really helping make wheat and hay and livestock here on the prairie—and you'd have no business unless that stuff got made and sold. Right?"

Ole rolled himself off the bale of hay and waddled the length of the scale platform and back to Carl.

"Captain, what about that red-taped, flub-dubbed, price-controlled, al-lo-cated, quo-tawed, puny little dab o' wire you was talkin' about?" Johnson said pleasantly, a grin flickering through the two-day-old gray stubble on his fat, red face.

Carl Yeoman whistled merrily as he walked back to his office. He had that good inside feeling that he was accomplishing something to make life better for those who live on the land as well as benefiting his business and Ole's—the same sort of feeling that his grandfather, Abner, had enjoyed when he had grubbed out the brush and brought to plow a new acre of prairie . . . the same triumphant feeling that had lifted the spirits of generations of Yeomans, one after another, all the way back to John Yeoman, who was the first to harvest food from American soil. The things he had said to Ole Johnson, though spoken in an offhand recourse to strategy, gave Carl a glimpse of his whereabouts on a new frontier—the agribusiness frontier.

He had said that he and Ole Johnson—the businessmen, the vendors of farm supplies—were helping operate the prairie's farms. He had linked himself, through his management of a farm supply company, to farming, and vaguely he realized that he was striving to take up the course of a good way of life that had been lost during the last years of his grandfather's farming. It was during his discussion with Ole Johnson that Carl sensed that somehow he was functioning in the capacity of an assistant to the present successors of the Abner Yeomans of a relatively prosperous earthbound era. Away from the land, he was nonetheless a real part of something that held a promise that farming might again provide for its participants a standard of living as satisfactory as that enjoyed by people in other walks of life.

Now the country was under the stress of war. This was putting an urgency to every phase of production throughout agriculture and industry. It was driving men to rush the advancement of technology; was spurring them to take immediate short cuts toward productive progress that otherwise might have required years to reach. The erratic, piecemeal transition from self-sufficient agriculture to a roughly outlined, partially organized frontier in agribusiness was suddenly becoming a disciplined, dynamic operation humming open-throttle in a determined effort to meet the ravenous appetite of a wartime economy.

The enemy's bombs dropping on Pearl Harbor had disabled the Carl Yeoman who dreamed of someday operating his own farm; but they had set up a new destiny for the Carl Yeoman who fitted into the supply segment of the agribusiness economy. Those bombs, by siphoning farm workers into the

155

armed services and war plants, helped plow a field that was being seeded to an array of improved supplies for farming that in time would grow a "crop of businesses" as big as the earthbound part of agriculture itself. Off the drawing boards and out of the factories poured a flood of labor-saving farm machines; out of test tubes and processing plants came more and better fertilizers, pest controls, vitamin concentrates, hormones, antibiotics, plastics, vaccines and medicines; from genetic research and mass-production breeding establishments came the amazing parentage for superior products that could be multiplied fabulously through such developments as plant hybridizing, artificial breeding of cattle and selection of superior families in poultry and livestock. And the better to serve his country in the grim task of surviving the big war, every farmer was urged to supply his farm with any or all of these things that would increase agricultural production.

Carl Yeoman returned to farming—not to plow and to harvest but to urge that each effective production supply be used wherever possible. Although he'd never heard the word, Carl Yeoman's life was devoted to agribusiness.

10.

IN THE OPENING MONTHS of 1943, the Allies were mopping up the successful North African campaign and preparing to probe for the vulnerable spot in the soft underbelly of Europe. On American farms, the plows were being readied to open fresh furrows on more of the fields where grass and legumes had grown in place of grain during the years when the government's soil conservation and acreage control programs had endeavored to reduce the output of cereal crops in order to bring them into balance with current consumption. The number and size of military-training camps became astounding. A farmer had a tough time finding a keg of nails or a load of lumber to put up a new hog house. The army, navy and air corps were deploying men by the tens of thousands to the fleets, the air-

fields and the outposts from which our great offensive could
be launched. American farming was urged to step up production of food in order to supply enormous quantities for our
distant military concentrations—and to replace the precious
cargoes that torpedoes sent to the bottom of the ocean. Factories of almost every kind were converted to war production,
and new plants by the thousands were constructed to expand
our output of war materials. The clamor for workers drew the
hired hands off the farms, took the housewives out of homes,
even brought the elderly and the handicapped out of retire-
ment for jobs in the war plants or to fill civilian occupations
vacated by those capable of handling more urgent assignments.
Taxes were increased and the withholding system for collecting income taxes was introduced. The public was urged to buy
bonds to finance the staggering cost of the war. Price and wage
controls were in effect. Priorities and allotments restricted the
distribution and use of materials and supplies. Necessities such
as food and fuel were rationed. All these things became a complicated counterbalance to the pressures that could wreck the
nation's economy with that explosive horror called inflation.

On the sixth of June, 1944, the Allied forces landed on the
beaches of Normandy. Factory workers were averaging better
than a dollar an hour—and with overtime pay, a week's wages
could be the price of a pretty good acre of farm land. American troops crossed the Rhine on March 7, 1945, and the collapse of Hitler's Germany was close at hand. American farmers
collected, on the average, about eleven cents a pound for beef
on the hoof; $1.46 for a bushel of wheat. The United States
had eight million men in its armed services and two thirds of
them were overseas. Some were making history in such places as
Iwo Jima and Okinawa. Corn sold for $1.07 a bushel in the
Northwest and hogs there didn't quite bring fourteen cents a

pound when they walked onto the packer's scales. On May 4 the Germans began to surrender. Wages in the factories averaged more than a nickel higher than two years before. On August 6, an American plane flew over Hiroshima and dropped an atomic bomb. Soon thereafter the United States faced its postwar readjustment problems.

Intermingled with the history-making events of the dangerous war years were many developments that revealed a great deal about agribusiness and its possibilities. But while all this was taking place, we were so preoccupied with the urgencies of the war effort that we hardly noticed what was happening to farming and its related businesses.

In the period of approximately twenty years prior to World War II, agriculture was in the throes of a physical transition into agribusiness—a transition roughed up by the rapid advance of mechanized farming, by the sudden increase in the potential productivity of farms, by the pitiful lack of balance between farming's productive capacity and the markets for farm products, and by the income anemia that afflicted farming during the decline of its earthbound status. Farming had now progressed beyond the point of no return, to economic self-sufficiency. Its increasing dependency on purchased supplies and on the off-farm storage and distribution of food and fiber products was spelling out a new era.

Although mentally we failed to recognize what was happening at the time, the wartime conditions provided new propulsion for the transition from agriculture to agribusiness . . . and in conjunction with this stepped-up tempo occurred certain phenomena that gave us a glimpse of the potentials of our agribusiness future. These phenomena fit three classifications. First, there was what we might call "open-throttle" farming— the reversal of a depression-bred, restrictive policy in agricultural output and in its stead a *zeal to produce* abundantly, efficiently and masterfully. Second, there was *adequate farm income*—enough for modernization of the farm plant and to provide the same kind of rewarding incentive for the farmer's all-out contribution to the nation's economy that stimulated the producer in factories and industries. Third, *rural employment* was satisfactorily adjusted. There were conditions that favored the comfortable, constructive transfer of people from less lucrative farming to more lucrative occupations elsewhere in our economy.

Although temporary and artificial, this wartime setting gave us an opportunity to see how our food and fiber economy could perform when we had the zeal to produce, plus adequate farm income, plus satisfactory rural employment occurring in unison and thus demonstrating the capacities of agribusiness in full swing. Just as electronic, aeronautic and atomic technology surged forward in response to the urgencies of war, so also did agribusiness accelerate its development in meeting the challenge of wartime emergencies. Only there was this significant difference: We recognized and understood electronics and aviation, but we did not fully comprehend that there was such a thing as agribusiness. So, of course, we did not understand it. We thought the economic factors relating to food and fiber were still mainly agricultural.

It was a trivial incident, the delivery of a pig to Carl Yeoman's young son David. Nobody who had a part in this event ever bothered to interpret it in any particular way. That it could possibly have anything to do with a strange, new concept of agricultural economics would have seemed fantastic. The only thing of any tangible significance was the pig. There she was. That she was there as a consequence of ten years of extraordinary complications for the human race was an incredible fact . . . and that she was to be the steppingstone over which a whole community would venture deep into agribusiness was a prospect no less remarkable. Yet here she was, a pig, destined for a new home as a result of depression, poverty, government aid to agriculture, the Pearl Harbor attack, the all-out effort to increase wartime food production, the recovery of farm income, and the transfer of farm people to off-farm occupations—all these events and circumstances converged to bring Ben Yeoman's grandson David a pig as a present on his tenth birthday.

The man was obviously embarrassed. "I owe you a pig," he blurted out as soon as the two customers left the salesroom of the Prairie Farm Supply Company.

"You what!" Carl Yeoman exclaimed.

He had known Ed Gaines casually during the four years of his management of the supply company. Sometimes they had visited about various things and Ed gave the impression of being quite complacent, calm and easygoing. But today Carl had noticed he seemed shy, not to say sheepish. Now Carl recalled that he had avoided conversation earlier when others were present, and the way he had been scanning the salesroom shelves told Carl that he was making a pretense of interest rather than actually shopping for something.

"Yep, I really owe you a pig, Carl," Ed repeated. He seemed tremendously relieved now that he had spoken these words.

"I don't catch on. Did we make a bet on something?"

"No, it wasn't like that. 'Way back, ten years ago, you took a job in the East, remember, and you left some of your registered hogs with your dad. Well, he wasn't making out with 'em too well and he was selling them off. I wanted to get a bred sow, but I didn't have any money for it. So your dad said,

'You take her, Ed, and sometime when Carl's back farmin' here, you can give him one to replace her.' " Ed paused a moment. "He always talked like it was a sure thing you'd be back on the farm with him in a year or two."

Carl turned and looked out the window.

"Well, you know, that sow raised us ten good pigs in her first litter. I picked out a nice little sow pig and called her 'Carl's pig'—and after a while she was an old sow. There was a 'Carl's pig' on the place year after year, granddaughters, then great-granddaughters of the sow I got from your dad."

"And you still have the same line of breeding?"

"Some of it, maybe, but it was the way I changed the breed that kept me from telling you about all this a long time ago."

Carl looked puzzled.

"The year before your dad died I had a wild idea about producing a fancy bacon hog. The Berks were too fat for that, I figured. Well, I read about some Danish hogs being tried by the Department of Agriculture. Landrace, they were called. So I made some connections and got ahold of a boar pig that was part Landrace and part Yorkshire. Of course, when I used him with the Berk sows, my pigs were just scrubs without registration papers. I was so dawgoned embarrassed about things being that way that I just couldn't offer you a pig when you came back here."

Carl laughed heartily.

"You know when a fella puts off something like this," Ed said seriously, "it gets pretty hard to get at it like a fella ought to. But your boy, David, and my Chris are pals, and David takes quite an interest in the pigs when he comes out to see Chris. So I got the happy idea that we could give your pig to David. Funny thing, we've got one that's due to have her litter on David's birthday. How about that?"

Carl looked thunderstruck. "Great Scott, Ed! What would we do with a pig—in town?"

"That's a handy little barn on your place. You'll have about two weeks to get things ready," Ed suggested. "And David sure wants to join the 4-H Club. Be wonderful if he could."

Ed Gaines hit the mark when he mentioned the 4-H Club. Carl grinned and said, "Seems I do remember something about pigs and 4-H Clubs. . . . Well, maybe the history of the Yeoman family is trying to repeat itself."

The pig that Ed Gaines delivered with his battered green pickup truck was white and long—longer by far than the wide-backed Berkshires Carl had raised in his youth. She walked down the tail-gate ramp of the truck and sniffed the straw scattered along the passageway to the barn. David clapped his hands and jumped up and down with excitement. "Take it easy, David," Carl admonished. "Everything here is strange to her. Just let her check up on anything she wants to examine." Hilda came from the house and stood at the entrance watching the proceedings. "Isn't she clean and white!" she exclaimed.

"Pigs'll stay clean if you give 'em a chance," Ed said.

Slowly they maneuvered the gilt into the old double horse stall that Carl and David had converted for a farrowing pen. They had placed a two by six across the space under the old manger, spiking it in position to let the baby pigs go under the manger and get out of their mother's way. They had cut a hole in the bottom of the manger and suspended an electric heat lamp through the hole. The light and warmth of the lamp would serve to attract the babies to the safety of the nursery.

"She's a beauty," Carl declared. "But tell me, what do you call this kind of hog?"

"Don't believe I could rightly say she's any kind—except an experimental model," Ed Gaines answered. "Someday, if we really get the type fixed so it will breed true, we'd like to call these hogs 'Tenderleans.' "

"Tenderleans—that's quite a name. Are they fairly uniform?"

"No. That's just the trouble. Only about a fourth of my pigs will be like this one. Some are short and fat; some are almost black; some are spotted. But now and then we find a sow that produces whole litters just about like this model here."

"You really have a breeding problem, don't you?"

"I sure have—but I can say this: when you dress a pig like this one, you get the finest pork you ever saw."

Young David named his sow "Princess." He was terribly excited over the prospect that she might give him a birthday present of a litter of baby pigs. On his birthday morning he was up at dawn and rushed to his parents' room but found that his father had dressed and gone out of the house. The eager youngster scrambled into his bathrobe and raced for the barn, losing one of his bedroom slippers on the way. He found his father in the pen with Princess. The sow was lying on her side, grunting in a rapid rhythm accompanied by the shrill squeaks and squeals of her babies.

"Sh, David. Don't make any noise," Carl cautioned. "You've got twelve little pigs, boy. Three with black spots and nine pure white."

"How many girl pigs?" David wanted to know.

"All the white ones are sow pigs, David."

"Gosh!" exclaimed the happy youngster.

In the days that followed, the Yeomans' barn became the mecca of young livestock lovers. David turned into a sort of straw boss with scarcely a chore to do by himself because there were always from one to half a dozen young volunteers pleading for a chance to wield the manure fork or measure the feed for Princess.

As the pigs grew to weaning age (eight weeks old) Carl began to worry.

"Young fellow," he said to David, "we have some decisions to make. You understand we can't keep all these pigs much longer."

"Oh, it's all fixed, Dad."

"What do you mean, fixed?"

"We're organizing a 4-H pig club. There's Billy and Jerry and . . ."

"Do their parents agree to this?"

"Well . . ." David hesitated.

Carl Yeoman decided his parental responsibilities had suddenly encompassed the destiny of twelve young pigs. He jotted down a list of David's pig-loving friends and began visiting their parents. Just as he had suspected, possession of a pig was a surprising outlook for most of them. Some said maybe it could be arranged; some said indeed not; and only a few received the idea with unqualified approval. Then Carl went to see the county's 4-H Club agent, Mrs. Adrian Coles.

The 4-H Clubs, with a membership of about two million youngsters ten to twenty-one years of age, are sponsored by the land-grant colleges and the United States Department of Agriculture through the Agricultural Extension Service. States and counties co-operate by employing extension specialists to organize and direct their 4-H Club projects. Each 4-H Club has its local volunteer leader, usually a farmer or homemaker whose personal qualities are such as to set a splendid example for the young members in respect to progressive outlook, public-spirited attitudes and pride in one's work. The 4-H

Clubs are independent of school activities and the projects they undertake involve training that is not related to classroom instruction. Incentives are furnished by an elaborate system of awards, prizes, trips and scholarships furnished for the most part by the public-relations funds of big businesses.

Mrs. Coles listened sympathetically to Carl's story. "I'm afraid our pig club projects have fallen by the wayside in recent years," she said. "Perhaps it's because it was necessary to put a woman in this job during the war, and livestock folks think they lose face in being led by a woman."

"More likely, folks were just too busy."

"You're very considerate, Mr. Yeoman, but the first problem is to find someone to lead this pig club. I think I'm talking to the best prospect there'll ever be."

Carl flushed. So that's how it stands, he said to himself. On his way from Mrs. Coles' office, carrying a packet of 4-H Club leader's materials, he seethed with exasperation. One thing for sure, he told himself, if I'm going to lead a pig club it's going to be a humdinger or I'll blow some fuses trying to make it so.

As Carl explored his new undertaking, he found that his major problem was to establish some kind of program that young boys could handle with a fair degree of consistency. He found his military training with its passion for uniform, standardized units caused him to be disdainful toward the hodge-podge of facilities and pig-raising methods proposed by his prospective club members. What he sought was some way to standardize the boys' projects so that their efforts could make uniform progress toward the most desirable goals.

It bothered Carl that the youngsters might attempt to grow their pigs in all sorts of makeshift quarters—and with similarly variable and questionable feeds. Furthermore, without some kind of plan or objective, it was likely that his club members would scatter their interests in a wide assortment of breeds and would attempt to produce many different kinds of live hog products ranging from feeder pigs to high-class breeding stock and thus lose out on the advantages of unity in their undertaking.

While pondering these problems, Carl hit on an old idea—the pig chain. Instead of buying pigs to start their projects, the boys and their parents could perhaps be persuaded to invest first in proper equipment. After that, arrangements could be made to furnish sow pigs to the members at no cost except the obligation to return a similar pig to the donors a year later. Proceeding on this course, Carl obtained plans for economical, practical hog houses. Then he scouted for quotations on the materials. He worked out a plan in which each member set up good, standard equipment to take care of a young pig, grow her to maturity and raise her litter to weaning age. He figured the probable feed costs and estimated the possible returns. The housing materials were going to cost about thirty dollars, the feed about sixty.

"You're way in over their heads," Hilda said skeptically. "You'd better decide you're setting up a club for the dads instead of the kids."

"Well," Carl contended, "this should be more businesslike than keeping pets. Either it's done right or nobody ought to try it. And it's not a bad idea to drag the dads into it, too."

With a sort of do-or-die attitude, Carl put his plans in his briefcase and set out on another round of visiting the parents of the youngsters David said were interested. Quite to his surprise, his interview, more often than not, ended in a pledge of enthusiastic co-operation. Then the story of his plans began to circulate and other boys and dads began to drop in at the Prairie Company store to ask about the pig club idea.

Much to his amazement, Carl found he had twenty-four boys and parents signed up when the organization effort had been completed. Now the problem was to find enough suitable pigs. Seven of the nine females in David's litter were highly satisfactory, and Carl's planning had not extended beyond these. In fact, he had doubted that he could place all of the seven. When he took his problem to Ed Gaines, however, Carl received assurance there'd be seventeen more good pigs available to the club.

Fathers and boys spent two busy Saturdays cutting and putting together the hog houses in the high-school shop. One dad was a carpenter, and he helpfully supervised the construction. Another was a trucker, and as fast as a house was finished he would deliver it to the owner. Two of the new houses were taken to the Yeoman homestead for the Turner boys. Dr. Turner, now back from the navy, had found his family so engrossed in country living that he had given up his campaign to move them back to town.

When all was ready and the pigs were distributed, two of David's gilts went to the Turner boys.

"Well, Mother, here we go again," Carl said, chuckling. "After twenty years, I'm disturbing the serenity of the farm again with one of my fancy pig projects. Think you can stand the wear and tear all over again?"

"Oh, I think so, Son," Betty answered. "My recollections of the first one are mostly pleasant—very pleasant, in fact. And I think it's going to keep me young watching the enthusiasm of Bobby and Henry. Besides, I think it's going to be as entertaining as a circus to watch Dr. Turner get himself involved in pig farming."

The Yeoman homestead had turned a corner in its financial

circumstances. Chet Burns was an exceptionally capable operator, just as Carl had predicted with the charts that had amused and annoyed his mother. The crops Chet harvested were the largest the farm had produced in a long, long time. Particularly big wheat yields came from the fields that had been growing alfalfa prior to the war. For five years, the price of wheat had been above one dollar a bushel, was up around $1.50 now, and farmers were assured the government would support the price at 90 per cent of parity until postwar adjustments were well along. These, then, were the years when Old Abner's land could be operated at its full capacity under modern, mechanized methods and its abundant production transformed into the means for providing its owners and operators with a living standard in harmony with the prosperity of other occupations. In addition to these favorable circumstances, Betty Yeoman benefited by the rent the Turners paid for their living quarters in the big farmhouse.

The Turners' rent money gave Betty Yeoman an opportunity to return to an old battlefield armed with new and effective weapons. It gave her a fighting chance to turn a heartbreaking defeat into eventual victory. She knew that Carl and Hilda would advise against her taking such a chance, but Betty Yeoman was a determined woman and if what she set her heart to do was more than she could master, then she alone would suffer the consequences of her folly.

Dr. Turner insisted that Betty be paid according to the amount the navy provided for family living quarters. This was $75 a month. That it would be so much never once occurred to Carl or Hilda. They were grateful that Nancy Turner and her sons were available to provide companionship for Betty, and they presumed that whatever the rental arrangement happened to be, the money involved was far less important than the other benefits. Under these circumstances, Betty realized that she had a windfall which she could exploit as she pleased—and be free from the protective cautiousness of her son.

She made her decision with the sudden recklessness of the frugal housewife who one day takes off her apron, plucks a fistful of bills out of the cracked teapot in the back of the cupboard, and rushes to the hat shop to buy a Paris-named creation priced five times higher than any other hat she'd ever bought. Betty Yeoman went straight to Chet Burns and, pledging him to secrecy, outlined her bold plan. Burns was a man with boundless good humor and a readiness to make a sporting event out of anything that was worth doing but so difficult that one needed real courage to try it. Would he back Betty's wild scheme? Chet Burns scowled at Betty in feigned indignation. Would he? He exploded in a hearty laugh and slapped her on the back so hard her straw bonnet flopped down over her eyes. "You just go to it, Mrs. Yeoman; Chet Burns'll do his part with pleasure." As she left, Chet made a V-for-victory sign with his fingers and gave her a kiss salute.

Betty's heart was bouncing when she entered the bank. When she left the president's office an hour later, there was a paper in her hand—a purchase agreement for the Colton place, and she held it so tightly that her knuckles turned white. She drove around by Chet Burns's farm on the way home and told him the news. Thereafter, Chet, serving as Betty's renter, farmed the 160 acres that Ben had rented during his ill-fated effort to expand his operations. When wheat sold for about a dollar a bushel, as it was doing when Betty started her ambitious program, it was the house rent the Turners paid that accounted for most of her progress in gaining equity in the Colton land, but now that wheat was up around $1.50 she was suddenly able to pay off sizable chunks of the principal. So far as Carl and Hilda knew, Chet Burns was farming the Colton place for the bank—and in a roundabout way, that's what he was doing.

11.

IN GENERAL, the spokesmen for major economic interests—including farm leaders, businessmen, public officials, and even professional experts—have been slow to comprehend the magnitude of the evolutionary forces which are converting *agriculture* into *agribusiness* and *farm problems* into *agribusiness problems*. They have been slow to recognize the inevitability of the changes which are inherent in the application of improved technology—changes in such factors as the size of unit, organization, managerial competence, technical skills, capital requirements, and market potentials. They have been prone to view maladjustments as temporary deviations from normal rather than as fundamental changes which will make the future unlike the past and which, accordingly, necessitate a constant re-evaluation of our food and fiber policy, taking into account all related functions, whether performed on or off the farm. Thus, a major factor limiting balanced progress and economic growth in the food and fiber phase of our economy has been the absence of a comprehensive well-defined and well-balanced agribusiness policy.

Of course, the need for re-examining our economic system with new perspective, oriented to progress, is not limited to agriculture but is universal—both on a national and international scale. The point is that nationally we have done a better job of making this transition in most other phases of the economy than in food and fiber. In general, nonagricultural business enterprises have tended to make decisions on the basis of the total operations of an industry—from preproduction determinations to the final sale of the products—to a greater degree than have the components of agribusiness. This is evidenced by the increasing size of business firms, the continuing trend toward vertical integration, the growth of trade associations, and similar co-ordinating efforts. While such developments also have characterized certain operations within agribusiness, they have not typified relationships generally, particularly between on-farm and off-farm functions.

The key to success in using the agribusiness approach to the solution of so-called farm problems lies in accurately anticipating changes brought about by technology and then taking appropriate action, with proper timing and dispatch, to turn such change to advantage both for agriculture and for the business functions related to it. The agribusiness approach to policy provides a comprehensive framework in which sound decisions can be made—decisions that will utilize our productive capacity in a manner that will advance national living standards as well as improve the economic status of our food

174

and fiber economy. Agribusiness progress is the result of tens of millions of decisions being made better, day after day, *ad infinitum*. These better decisions are the cumulative product of millions of farmers, businessmen and public officials making wiser choices as to alternatives when they view problems in an agribusiness frame of reference.

The story of the Yeomans is, of course, fictitious in that the characters here depicted never really lived. However, it is a realistic story in the sense that the episodes here portrayed are representative of what did take place as our food and fiber economy evolved from the era of agriculture to that of agri-business.

The ingenuity, resourcefulness, and courage displayed by Carl Yeoman and his associates in developing the Tenderlean hogs is typical of that shown by our better farm leaders and businessmen in a variety of important ventures . . . far-sighted rural youth programs, effective public relations such as Farm-City Week, co-operative enterprises, marketing agreements, promotion programs with strong financial support such as those of the National Cotton Council, the American Dairy Association, and the sales campaigns for plentiful foods which co-ordinate merchandising factors from farm to consumer.

Of course, not all ventures of this type have been successful. Much has depended upon the quality of leadership in the given situation and the degree to which an agribusiness viewpoint has prevailed. However, even with all of their limitations and shortcomings, these agribusiness-type efforts have served as a valuable foundation on which to launch a sounder and more prosperous future for the food and fiber part of our economy.

In the spring of 1947, Carl realized that his Prairie 4-H Pig Club was approaching a crisis—a predicament precipitated by its early success. If, as Carl had first anticipated, half a dozen youngsters had taken up the project, the fifty or so pigs their sows produced would readily find a market as feeder stock sold in pairs and trios to farmers who grew their own pork. But now there were twenty-four boys, twenty-four sows, and prospects of more than 200 Tenderlean piglets to be marketed. All told, it was a much bigger business enterprise than anyone had realized.

Carl made contact with farmers' livestock auctions in surrounding localities and learned that these would be receptive to consignments of weanling stock if they could be offered in uniform lots of about forty head, enough to make a carload unit when fed out by the buyer. Quite without his planning it, many of the boys' parents attended the pig club's meetings regularly. Now that the project had swelled to commercial proportions, Carl counted himself lucky to have so many parents in close touch with the club's problems. Nevertheless, there was protocol in Carl's pig club, and instead of presenting his findings about the auction markets directly to the club's meeting, Carl took pains to brief the boys' marketing committee on the facts, and its young chairman stood up and gave the group a report that was exceedingly well presented.

A lad with penny-size freckles rose and said, "Mr. President, this is a fine plan, but my folks want to know when they can have some of our good Tenderlean pork to eat. I'd like to see us consider a plan that would answer that, too." The president asked if any parents present wished to comment on this suggestion.

"Mr. President, I sure do," said a father who was one of Carl's suburban neighbors, a gas station owner with two boys in the club. "Fred and Jimmy have had us drooling for Tenderlean pork ever since they got their pigs. You know, we didn't know that pigs could be such respectable things until Mr. Yeoman showed the boys how to raise stock the right way. Now I say if anybody's going to eat these choice, beautiful pigs, let the home folks in on it, whatever you do." This proposal stirred up considerable enthusiasm and a motion was passed creating a committee of boys and dads to draft plans for a meat hog project to be operated in conjunction with the sow-and-litter program.

Then another father stood up and said, "Mr. President, if I'm not out of order, I'd like to ask the club to consider formation of an auxiliary association for grownups." Some of the dads laughed loudly, but the speaker continued. "Yes, I know, this is reversing the usual practice. It's customary for the adults to start a livestock association that later sponsors a 4-H Club. But I don't see why it can't work the other way round. Let the boys here, through their fine club, sponsor a pig club for grownups." Now both the boys and many of their dads laughed heartily. "But I'm not joking," the man insisted. "I'm a farmer, as you know, and I think there are a lot of farmers around here who could make pigs a profitable side line if we went at it right—like Mr. Yeoman, here, is teaching the young folks to do. I can see where there are great possibilities in a concerted, organized program—just as was brought out in your marketing committee report. There isn't much of a future for individual farmers here on the prairie to take a fling at a small livestock project all alone. But if we organized our operations and did some careful planning, I can see how we could do a great deal better. What's more, I think there's a wonderful opportunity in these Tenderlean pigs. They are longer and leaner, and while I haven't had a chance to eat any Tenderlean pork—much as I'd like to try it—I think it's a good bet that it will be mighty good eatin'. I think farmers around here could make some money producing high-quality hogs like these Tenderleans."

To Carl's great surprise, other farmers spoke endorsing the idea.

"Seems to me, Mr. President," one of them said, "that it would be a pity to ship away so many of the good sow pigs you boys will have in your litters this spring. We ought to keep the best of this stock here on the prairie and make ourselves a way to benefit from it. I don't think many farming communities get a chance such as we've got—and I'd like to see us do something about it before it's too late."

Another farmer said, "Mr. President, I think now's the time for action. I'd like to point out that the hog market is up to pretty near twenty cents—and I think there's going to be money in hogs."

Carl fidgeted. It bothered him that the fathers were butting in on the boys' meeting more than he thought was proper. Before he could think of a way to check the intrusion of the adults, the boys had passed another motion creating a committee of boys and dads to organize—of all things— a senior Tenderlean association to be sponsored by the junior group.

To Carl's consternation, the plans he had developed to provide "a way out"—as he confided to Hilda—for the boys to liquidate their sow-and-litter projects and get set to repeat a conservative program had led to exactly the opposite outlook. Carl had expected there'd be some discouragement, disillusionment and waning of interest among the boys, with the result that the second year of the pig club would see quite a shakedown in the membership. He thought that perhaps a dozen boys would stick with the project—and that would mean that for Carl, the leader, and the boys and their dads the whole program would be a pleasant hobby instead of something verging on a substantial business enterprise. A few boys did drop out, but to Carl's bewilderment, there was a waiting list of others anxious to take over the stock and equipment of the ones who for various reasons were resigning from the club.

When the committees on the new projects began to function, Carl found that he was chief-of-staff of Operation Tenderlean Pigs, and far from being a small, back-yard project for little boys like his son David, this proposition was becoming a challenge to the traditional operations of farms all over the prairie.

"Nobody knows if this is going to work out," Carl grumbled to Hilda when he came home from a committee meeting that had lasted almost until midnight. "Talk about something going 'hog wild'—that's just what's happening."

"You've said it takes vision and enthusiasm to make group action successful," Hilda remarked. "Well, what are you worrying about? Seems to me these people have a 'vision' of what they think are real possibilities. And they've got enthusiasm, that's for sure."

"Yeah," Carl said disconsolately. "But this pig scheme is getting out of hand. They've got me pegged as the leader of it, and the fact is, I can't even catch up with it. I'm scared this will be known as 'Carl Yeoman's Folly' when the thing collapses."

"Well, just make sure it doesn't collapse," Hilda said cheerfully.

All right, Carl told himself, if these people are so eager to plunge into a new kind of livestock operation, then the thing to do was to set the standards so high and the regulations so tough that the timid and halfhearted would be scared off, while those with real determination would have a reasonable prospect of being successful because they would be willing to use the best management practices. Acting on this strategy, Carl solicited the most up-to-date recommendations of the county agent, the extension livestock specialist and the professors of animal husbandry at the state college. From the bulletins they supplied and their letters outlining suggestions, Carl drafted a plan for the market hog program (the production of butcher stock) that was severely specific. It gave no quarter for casual practices and haphazard procedures. The housing, while simple and efficient, called for lumber and hardware amounting to the value of the pork from a pig grown to market size, butchered, and the hams, shoulders and bacon sides cured and smoked. Other equipment included an automatic waterer attached to a metal oil drum, a homemade self-feeder costing ten dollars for materials and a roll of galvanized woven wire fencing. The boy or man undertaking the project also must be prepared to provide two hundred pounds of high-protein supplement feed to blend with five or six hundred pounds of rolled barley. And whether or not the feeder could profitably trade his grain for gains put on by his live hog was a real gamble. Now, Carl thought, this way of shooting for perfection will water down the hopes of the overenthusiastic . . . and this runaway enthusiasm will shrink until participation is down to about a dozen fathers and sons willing to indulge seriously in a livestock hobby for their own particular reasons.

The gilts in the hands of the 4-H members delivered their litters and the average litter was 11.5 pigs—somewhere around three pigs more than ordinary averages. Carl had to admit that these figures constituted vital statistics that almost every patron of the Prairie Farm Supply Company wanted to talk about. Very well, Carl decided, let's see if this auspicious beginning will stand up in the second lap—the one in which pigs are weighed at fifty-six days of age and their weights become a bench mark in evaluating bloodlines and management.

Carl visited each boy's project and checked on the arrangements to induce the baby pigs to begin eating a starting ration from a trough partitioned away from the mother sow's quarters. While making the rounds, Carl wondered which it was that motivated his thoroughness: his army officer custom of inspecting procedures or a secret desire to have the boys grow their pigs to commendable weights. Whichever it was, the results were notable. An ordinary eight-week-old weanling pig weighs around 25 pounds, but the average of the 4-H Club's Tenderlean litters was a 36.7-pound pig . . . and the average litter weaned numbered 9.75 pigs—far ahead of the ordinary average. Jim Brown, who witnessed many of the weighings, was emphatically impressed. So was the county agent and the state livestock specialist when they learned the way the Prairie 4-H Pig Club's first litter records had turned out.

Ed Gaines rigged up a handy trailer to carry his boar, and when the 4-H boys reported their sows had come in heat after the pigs were weaned, he brought the boar to the boys' places and charged only five dollars for the breeding service. Carl clapped his hands to his head and exclaimed to Hilda, "This thing is never going to end!"

Every one of David's chain pigs "came back" in cash instead of "in kind."

There was a farmer, or in two instances a new 4-H Club member, who was ready to pay the club's standard price of thirty dollars for the opportunity to buy a selected gilt of the Tenderlean stock. David's seven "staked-out" gilts brought in $210 cash, and Carl somewhat grudgingly admitted that the first anniversary of the project netted David Yeoman a profit.

The senior pig club was organized as the Tenderlean Pork Association. Ed Gaines was elected president . . . and Carl Yeoman was the unanimous choice for secretary-treasurer.

Forty-two farmers became charter members and they all agreed to follow precisely the same sow-and-litter program Carl had devised for the 4-H members, except that half a dozen of them purchased bred sows and gilts from Ed Gaines's herd and thus attained a head start in production of stock for sale. The shrink in 4-H membership that Carl had anticipated did not materialize, and instead, the junior group increased to thirty-one members. With seven new members each requiring a sow pig, and forty-two senior members ready to take from one to ten young females, the charter members of the 4-H Club found they had a market for 112 of their weanling sow pigs.

Twenty juniors and seniors enrolled in the butcher hog program, each feeding three barrows precisely the way Carl said the experts advised. From the 4-H Club's litters only forty-two weanlings were left over to be trucked to an auction, and since these had been culled out in making selections for the Prairie projects, Carl insisted that they be described as "Tenderlean rejects" when sold. "The time will come when we will want to market our good stock in the auctions," Carl insisted, "and we must make it plain that this first lot is substandard compared with our real product."

This did, indeed, make an impression at the auction. Neither the officials nor the prospective buyers could quite understand why a consignor would deliberately "knock" his product before it was sold. The result was that the Tenderlean pigs were the most talked-about offering the auction had ever received, and they sold for $13.75 a head—a very good price.

Carl contended that the butcher stock should be dressed as soon as the live hog weighed 200 pounds. At that weight, the hams, bacon sides and loins for chops and roasts were in the range of sizes most generally favored by consumers . . . and equally important, the pig usually reached the peak of his efficiency in converting feed into pork. At heavier weights, it required progressively more feed to make a pound of meat. Furthermore, if the object was to produce lean, tender pork, the younger, lighter pig was preferable to an older, heavier and fatter hog. In order to avoid casual guessing as to weights, Carl rigged up a weighing crate that fitted his company's portable platform scale. This made an outfit that was easily carried in a pickup truck, and when the butcher stock was nearing the 200-pound size, Carl or Ed Gaines began making the rounds on summer evenings, weighing hogs and charting their progress.

The first trio of Tenderlean barrows was butchered by Stewart Williams at the local locker plant when the pigs were five months and two days old. They made a pound of live hog out of 3.4 pounds of feed. David's trio was ready at five months and twenty days, and they used 3.6 pounds of feed to make a pound of live hog. The last of the sixty barrows were dressed when they were six months and nine days old, and there was one lot that required 4.3 pounds of feed to produce a pound of pig on the hoof. Ed Gaines winced at these figures. "My Tenderleans are a long way from being uniformly good, aren't they?" he remarked.

"Well," Carl observed, "nobody should expect that everything is going to be perfect right off the bat in a livestock project such as this. That's why I've been trying to keep our feet on the ground. Some of our figures are very encouraging, but— as you can see, Ed—a lot of careful, scientific breeding work has to be done to make Tenderleans consistently good."

"Sure," Ed said, "but what's to prevent our doing just that?"

Carl sighed. "Gosh, do you realize, Ed, that swine breeders have been making a pass at this super-pork idea for at least twenty years . . . and except for little flash-in-the-pan projects like ours, it hasn't budged a bit in all that time. Why, when I was a kid and bought my first hogs, those registered Berkshires, the farm papers and livestock magazines were full of articles about lean pork and efficient strains. But what happened? These ideas hit a snafu somewhere, and farmers went right on producing lard, and packers paid almost the same price for a hog a hundred pounds overweight for best efficiency and much too fat to please consumers who wanted to eat leaner, better pork. No, Ed, the policies that influence breeders, hog farmers, packers and consumers are all mixed up. If you and I think we can straighten them out all of sudden, we're just dreaming."

"Carl, I think you're a dawgoned pessimist."

"Call me a realist, but at least I'll do this, Ed: we're in the middle of something—in this Tenderlean program—and I'll do my level best to make it successful. I want us to be conservative—so that most of the folks who are involved are not expecting anything above the average. I mean the real average as we measure it. I want it to be a pleasant surprise when somebody beats the average. I don't want anybody to be so oversold on this Tenderlean program that he thinks it's going to lead right up to a pot of gold at the end of a pretty rainbow."

"That makes sense," Ed agreed.

The Tenderlean clubs, junior and senior, joined forces for a roast pork banquet celebrating the completion of the first butcher hog project. Members who grew the butcher stock each proudly contributed a roast. Guests included all the local farm and business notables—the officers of the Farm Bureau and the Chamber of Commerce, the county agricultural extension service staff, the bankers, merchants and newspaper people, managers of nearby co-operative livestock auctions, fieldmen for a big packing company, and men from the feed mills that supplied Carl's company and its rival the Johnson Brothers, and representatives of two of the hog breed associations which naturally were inclined to take a dim view of the upstart Tenderlean breeding operations.

The remarks of the guests who spoke ranged from unbridled enthusiasm to damning the whole proposition with faint praise. The local patriots viewed with pride the effort to diversify the prairie's farming and to initiate interest in a product of superior quality. The feed company representatives outlined the prodigious efforts going on in the science of nutrition and told how this research was beginning to improve the efficiency with which all forms of livestock could be produced.

The men from the swine registry associations credited the purebred stock in the ancestry of the Tenderleans as being the source of the qualities found to be so commendable in the pork served at this banquet, and they suggested that sooner or later adventuresome breeders straying from the fold in projects like the Tenderleans would by-and-by see the folly of their course and settle back to raising registered hogs.

The packer's representative explained that it was his company's obligation in the scheme of things to provide a market for whatever kind of critter happened to show up in a stockyard. Performing as it did a great range of services between farms and meat markets and collecting hardly more than a penny a pound for all its processing operations, it should be forgiven for not indulging in the extremely expensive promotion necessary to create a market for an exceptional product that would be available in a very limited quantity. Furthermore, he said, the opinions on superiority in meats were not entirely consistent; hence, to be practical about the whole idea, the packer selected light, heavy, fat and lean hogs within a rather narrow range of prices and sorted the carcasses to suit the buyers' whims as to weights and qualities. That way, he explained, the packer could always find enough light hogs or lean hogs in a week's run to supply the customers wanting these characteristics . . . so there was no urgency for the packer to promote a special kind of pork to a greater extent than other kinds. But, said the packer, he was pleased, of course, to see so much interest in producing good hogs efficiently.

When the banquest was over, Ed Gaines said to Carl, "I don't know yet whether I should be blue or mad . . . or just damn your pessimistic hide and let it go at that."

"Well, I told you there was hard going ahead, didn't I? Personally, I'm glad some of the speakers shot us down instead of letting this project go flying high before it's grown any tail feathers."

"Guess I thought we'd have a beautiful love feast—with everybody so happy you'd lose your pessimism, Carl."

"Not pessimism—realism! I'm glad it wasn't just a lot of gushing praises. Now we should all have our eyes open . . . and we're in a lot better shape to tackle a proposition as tough as this."

It remained for Kirk McGregor, editor of the prairie's weekly newspaper, to sum up the situation. His editorial was titled "The Impossible Will Take a Little Longer." "Any of you," he wrote, "who were lucky enough to attend the local pig growers' party Friday evening sampled the best roast pork it's been our privilege to chew. No, chew isn't the word. It was too tender to need more than a light caress from our silver-filled molars. Along with the delicious pork, however, we heard a lot of talk about pigs and pork. Much of it we didn't understand. But we did come away with the idea that we had just feasted on something that couldn't be. If we understood some of the experts correctly, folks hereabouts are just kidding themselves. There isn't going to be any such thing as nice, lean, juicy, tender pork for us, the consumers. Pigs is pigs. Pork is pork. And don't you waste your time tinkering with it, Ed Gaines and Carl Yeoman. Well, now, these local men may be just like the bumblebee who doesn't know any better than to fly, even though engineers say a design such as his can't possibly be air-borne. Through the leadership of the pig club officers, we ate some impossible pork. Our guess would be that people all over this country are waiting for this pork to show up on their dinner tables. Like they say, the difficult is easy, but the impossible may take a little longer."

Although the agribusiness frontier was not yet something with a name, there was plenty of mud from this new territory collecting on Carl Yeoman's boots. Born to the farming or production segment of it, Carl next found his occupation had settled him in its supply segment . . . and now, through the development of a hobby which he could share with his young son, he was becoming involved in its market segment. That these three parts of the pattern of his life had more than a happenstance relationship, one to the other, did not occur to Carl.

12.

As the passing years moved us closer to the midpoint of the twentieth century, the single word most aptly applied to American farming was *change*. It must be remembered that down through the centuries agriculture was never really static, although it remained a relatively stable enterprise throughout its earthbound era. Then, during the period of transition to the agribusiness era, new developments began occurring more and more frequently and with greater and greater significance. Before these changes became extensive, however, an American farmer could have swapped places with Horatius, who plowed his fields in ancient Rome 2,500 years ago, and each would have found his tasks and objectives almost as familiar as they would have been on his neighbor's farm. But in the agribusiness era, changes came about in American farming that made it something quite unlike the agriculture known to Horatius.

The machines used in the fields, the chemicals that fertilized plants and controlled the insects and diseases that afflicted them, the manufactured feeds with their minute ingredients of vitamins, minerals and antibiotics, the vaccines, medicines and hormones—all these were changes that came with agribusiness, and they would have puzzled and appalled Horatius. Their counterparts, as he knew them, were draft animals, carved wooden implements, dung heaps, grains and fodders and a few herbs—all of them things the farmer produced on his own land. The laboratories, the factories, the chemistry and technology that were now producing the myriad of new supplies used every day by the American farmer changed his agriculture into something that extended far beyond the farm's boundary fences.

Likewise, much of what a farmer produced no longer remained on the land for conversion and consumption there. Horatius would, indeed, have been astonished to see how little of the farm's production of crops and animals remained for the farmer's use. A cart to haul away the small proportion of food, fiber and hides not needed at home, a humble spot in the market place where the farmer could trade these products—for a long, long time these were the earthbound era's concession to agriculture's interest in the businesses that transported, handled, stored, processed, refined, distributed and merchandised products originating on the farm. But the changes came— briskly sometimes, hesitantly sometimes—but enough of them to create something far bigger in its economic dimensions than agriculture itself.

Midway in the twentieth century we watched our farming change rapidly year by year. We could look back and see that the changes had come faster and faster . . . and if we chose to look to the future, it was plain to be seen that the developments of the past had been but the steppingstones to future change. But in no single important phase of agriculture had the ultimate of progress been achieved or even approached. Powered by the ever-increasing list of scientific discoveries and by the constantly improving applications of technology, farming was picked up bodily by the flood tide of progress. This was true whether one considered plant and animal breeding, cultural practices, land and water conservation, equipment design, disease control, plant nutrition and fertilization, preservation and transportation, the various phases of marketing and market development. In all probability the future of agriculture will be even more characterized by change than was the past.

Of course, this element of change was not limited to agriculture . . . nor will it be in the future. It has been and promises to continue to be true of our whole economy. This needs to be so, if America is to be strong, if our economy is to be resilient and dynamic, and if we are to create new jobs for our growing population and at the same time continue gradually to improve our over-all standard of living.

Change was rampant in the farming on his native prairie, Carl Yeoman was aware. One could see it in the new machines . . . the shifting uses to which the land was put . . . the uprooting of old customs and practices to seek a better income . . . the increasing diversity of supplies the farmers used . . . the closing out of inefficient farms and the expanding operations of the ones that were managed more successfully.

Leaning on the counter in his farm supply salesroom, Carl flipped the pages of a wholesaler's catalogue, pausing now and then to study a page that described new equipment, new gadgets that made farming easier or enabled a man to improve his operations. He heard the crunch of tires on the gravel in the company's parking space and when he looked out the window he was surprised to see the Johnson Brothers' yellow service truck. Ole Johnson, fat and clumsy, rolled out of the driver's seat and moved ponderously toward the salesroom door.

"Mornin', Carl," Ole said, puffing.

"Good morning, Ole," Carl genially responded.

They exchanged opinions about the fitness of the early May weather for haying, and then Ole grinned and said, "Carl, I've got the hottest idea for making money on prairie farms you ever heard of."

"I'm all ears," Carl said, a slightly laconic tone in his voice.

"Irri-gation!"

Carl blinked. He was about to say, "Fine, but where we do get the water?"

"We'll drill wells and pump water; then we'll pipe it all over hell's half-acre with aluminum pipe, big pipe, four-inch stuff. With sprinklers fed from these big pipes, a fella can water forty acres just like 'twas a lawn in his front yard." Ole beamed.

"I've read about sprinkler irrigation," Carl said. "But it's mighty expensive, isn't it?"

"It shore is, but that's all right. Now I suppose you wonder why I'm here, blabbin' to my competition. Well, Carl, remember 'way back when we got together on a carload of barbed wire? Now I've been thinkin' about this irrigation plan for a long time and I come to the conclusion that the smart thing to do is to work it so your outfit and mine can concentrate on different parts of the program instead of each of us spreadin' thin over the whole layout and being competitors right down the line. See?"

"Go on."

"Well, first of all, there's wells to drill. Now that kind of thing is an old Johnson specialty—like threshin' used to be. Wells cost money—maybe five or ten thousand dollars for a farm. In the beginning, folks are going to be scared off by such figures, but Johnson Brothers can finance a few installations, and if they pay like I expect they will, then folks'll dig into the old mattress and fetch the money, or get bold enough to go see bankers about mortgages to get it. Then there's pumps to buy. Selling and servicing them is another good Johnson specialty. But there's also this aluminum pipe to buy. I figure that's where your outfit belongs in the picture. You handle the pipe and sprinklers. It's easier for us Johnsons to use our capital to get the drilling program rolling than it would be for your company to do that. On the other hand, Prairie Supply can handle pipe with its capital same as it does wire and stuff. So, what's the matter with usin' our heads and just about doublin' the irri-gation business both outfits'll do?"

"Sounds pretty good, Ole."

"Well, what are we waitin' for?"

"This requires some approval from our stockholders, Ole."

"Oh, sure, sure. But let's push 'er along. And that reminds me, Carl, I'm really steamed up about this irri-gation idea and my brother and I are goin' right at it to drill wells on our land, fast as we can . . . and what we want to do, too, is put at least one well on your home place. No better way to show the prairie folks we're teamed up together and puttin' our faith in this new irri-gation. See?" The big man leaned closer. "Know somethin', Carl? You'll take four or five times as much wheat or alfalfa off a watered acre as a dry one. Think 'er over, boy."

The Johnsons sank five wells on their farms, and while two of them were of little value, the other three provided an abundance of water. The REA ran its electric lines to these wells, and the Johnsons installed powerful automatic pumps. The Prairie Farm Supply Company brought in a truckload of aluminum pipe sections and helped connect the sprinklers for a trial of the system.

"Stand back, Ole, or you'll get soaked," Carl shouted when he noticed the big man was standing a few feet from a sprinkler, fascinated, like a small boy watching the fuse of a firecracker.

"Let 'er rain!" Ole bellowed.

The pump buzzed and water hissed through the long line of pipe. A few droplets falling from the sprinkler arms sparkled like diamonds in the sunlight. Soon little streams of water squirted upward, balked, dwindled, then sputtered as they rose again in a higher arc and the sprinkler heads began to turn. The water made a *flick-flick* sound as the moving stream came in contact with the ankle-high alfalfa. On bare spots of ground, the big drops of water lifted tiny dust clouds as they fell. Big Ole Johnson took off his harvester's helmet and let the beads of water bounce off his bald head.

"Jeez, ain't this great," he roared.

Carl and his sisters, Sue and Meg, had left their share of the farm's income as stand-by capital for emergencies or improvements, and out of this they agreed to invest in a well. Quite to their relief, they found their mother ready and willing to sink a well on her part of the property. And then came the big surprise. Betty Yeoman revealed how she had purchased the Colton property . . . and that she now owned it free and clear. Furthermore, she wanted a trial well drilled on it.

All three of the irrigation wells on the Yeoman properties gave good results—enough so to treble the tonnage of alfalfa hay Chet Burns harvested from the watered land. When wheat was planted in the fall, Carl and Chet decided to try an application of nitrogen, to be followed by a thorough watering with the sprinkler system. The new grain sprang up quickly, lining the drill rows with the rich green feathering of robust wheat seedlings. And with the price of wheat jockeying about $2.75 a bushel, the prospects created by the new equipment and methods put a song in the heart of Carl Yeoman.

Great changes were taking place on farms all over the prairie —exciting changes.

The white hog houses of the Tenderlean projects dotted the green plots of alfalfa adjacent to the farmsteads along the county roads, and Carl marveled at the way they had become a distinguishing feature of the landscape. Every one of these neat, white piggeries, however, contained a problem, Carl was well aware. The transition of prairie farming from crops alone to the combination of crops and livestock was poised now between rash adventure and practical development. The Tenderlean enthusiasts had met the challenges of supply and production, but there remained the crucial problem of developing a market for the prairie's potential output of superior pork.

Carl thought about the newspaper editor's name for it: the impossible pork. He might have thought, too, of the fact that pigs were brought to this continent in 1539 by the Spanish explorer Hernando De Soto, and that they had grub-staked his expedition on its march from Florida to Arkansas. Better than trinkets and cutlery for bartering passage through the Indian hunting grounds, the descendants of De Soto's two boars and thirteen sows helped determine the course of American history—indeed, made history, because mankind, Spanish or Indian, was happy to eat pork. Now, four centuries later, Carl Yeoman's problem was to find the people who would likewise be happy to eat pork, the prairie's Tenderlean pork.

He talked to Stewart Williams, the local locker plant proprietor, about a marketing program, but Stewart shrugged and said, "My gosh, Carl, there are ten or twenty times more pigs grown around here now than the people here can eat. Why don't you just ship 'em out to a market somewhere?"

"Maybe that's what we'll have to do," Carl admitted, "but we'll never get our idea through to the consumer if we do that. Our Tenderleans will be mixed in with all other pork and nobody who buys pork chops or roasts will know our story."

"If you could just bring customers here to see what you're doing," Williams suggested, "then they'd appreciate this Tenderlean pork."

"You've hit it!" Carl exclaimed. "Let's get some samples ready and we'll invite pork buyers from surrounding cities to come here for an 'open house,' as they call it in new stores or factories. We can take them on a tour of the prairie farms, show 'em your plant and give 'em a feast on Tenderlean pork."

"Might work," Williams said, but there was skepticism in his voice.

Carl presented his plans to the officers of the junior and senior pig clubs and received enthusiastic support. The clubs appointed committees to handle the details, and Carl worked up a list of restaurant owners, chain-store meat buyers and independent retailers to whom he mailed invitations for a Labor Day "Tenderlean Country Visit." The program was to open with a luncheon featuring Tenderlean sausage and bacon; then the visitors would be conducted on a tour of five farms and 4-H projects, each place selected to exemplify a phase of the Tenderlean project. At six o'clock, the guests would be treated to a roast pork banquet—and when they departed, each would receive a pound of sausage and a pound of bacon, neatly labeled "Tenderlean." Carl booked reservations at the hotel and the town's three motels. The newspaper editor prepared the prairie's first "extra," consisting of eight pages devoted almost entirely to stories describing the Tenderlean project—and as a special salute to public relations for the enterprise he planned to hold the forms open until guests arrived so that he could list all the visitors in a half-page display welcoming them to "Tenderlean Country." In addition to his regular subscribers, he planned to print 200 copies to give to the hundred or more visitors.

It was a great idea—except that Carl received a handful of acknowledgments expressing regrets that the invitations could not be accepted, and just one single acceptance.

"Thanks. I'll be there," said a note from Max Lukas. There were twelve roadside diners and two large downtown restaurants in the Lukas chain. Far from being distinguished places to dine, they were establishments that lived up to their homely motto—"A square deal and a square meal." For two days, Carl and the crestfallen committee debated what to do—swallow their pride and call off the "open house" or wince with embarrassment and treat Max to a private tour. Nobody seemed to think of a good explanation to give Mr. Lukas . . . and time ran out on the opportunity to retreat.

Max Lukas, a short, stocky man, parked his Cadillac in front of the hotel at eleven o'clock, registered and inquired where he could see some Tenderlean pork. The flustered clerk at the hotel said he thought the place to do that would be the locker plant, and he gave Max directions to find it. Stewart Williams was busy filling two-pound freezer cartons with the sausage that the Tenderlean promoters had expected to serve at their big luncheon which now was canceled. He looked up from his work to find Max Lukas standing at his elbow. The visitor said "Goot morning," quite casually, but he kept his hands in his pockets and his eyes on the tray of sausage meat. Williams began a somewhat mechanical recital of his locker plant's operations in connection with the Tenderlean project. For a long time, Lukas listened without making any comment. But when Williams finished the tray he was packing, Lukas suddenly began asking questions: what cuts were in the sausage . . . how big were the pigs . . . what recipe was used for seasoning?

Members of the Tenderlean committees who had expected to be hosts to a hundred visitors that day soon discovered that their lone guest could ask as many questions as they'd expect from a busload of people casually interested in the lean-pork idea. When Carl announced that plans had been made for the group to have lunch at the Main Street Café, Max Lukas spoke up quickly. "Please, vould you ask dem not to cuke anyting till ve come. I vould like, please, to cuke for us myzelf."

In the café kitchen, Max donned a chef's hat and apron. The moment a spatula was in his hand he lost his solemn, deadpan expression and became a jolly extrovert . . . singing German ballads and jesting merrily with the café's staff. When the platters of sausage, bacon and scrambled eggs arrived at the table, Max came out of the kitchen, his face aglow from both the stove's heat and the warmth of his enthusiasm. "Vell, gentlemens," he said, beaming, "now I tell you vot. Ve haf someting! Yes, py chingo, ve haf someting!"

There was no doubt about it . . . Max was a master chef, and the way he prepared the Tenderlean products brought forth every element of their quality. The bacon lay on the luncheon plates in bright, red-brown strips, delicately crisp and rippled. The sausage cakes were plump and moist, their savory richness giving the dining room an appetizing fragrance. Lightly crusted, tender as a peach, they were delightful to look at and a pleasure to eat.

Max Lukas obviously enjoyed meeting the pigs, too. He said it was a "voondervul" idea to show prospective customers the whole program behind a food product—especially when a thorough inspection could produce the favorable impressions he was getting by seeing every phase of the Tenderlean project. He climbed in and out of pigpens all afternoon. He learned to scratch a sow's ear as a reward for letting him pick up one of her baby pigs. He studied very intently the 4-H record books the Turner boys showed him, and in his thick Germanic accent he made them quite a complimentary speech on the virtues of learning businesslike habits early in life. He listened while Ed Gaines explained the breeder's part in the Tenderlean project . . . even tasted the hog rations while Carl explained how the stock was fed. Inasmuch as the banquet plans had collapsed, Carl invited Max, Ed Gaines, Stewart Williams and the Turner boys, Bob and Henry, to have a roast pork supper at his home. Stewart prepared a handsome crown roast and Hilda won hearty praise from Max for the way she cooked it.

"Well, Mr. Lukas, we've exposed you to everything from squeal to gravy in our Tenderlean program," Ed Gaines said as Hilda refilled the coffee cups. "I hope we didn't bore you too much."

Max chuckled. "Today I've got me an answer to that remark . . . I see vot a boar truly is!" Then he added, "To me, it vas a very interesting day, and I appreciate the invitation." Max Lukas took the wrapper off a cigar and pointed it at Ed Gaines while he recited his interpretation of the breeder's role in the development of a lean-meat type of pig; then he pointed to Carl and recalled the information he had picked up about the feeds and equipment used in growing the Tenderlean stock. He turned to the boys, David Yeoman, Bob and Henry

Turner, and commented that the community's pork enterprise was already preparing for its future development. He pointed to Stewart Williams and reviewed the processor's part in the project. Tapping his chest with the end of the cigar, Max described his interest in finding food for people to eat and in finding people to eat the food he could supply. He paused and, using both arms to form a circle, he said, "All of us here—ve are like one big machine that vorks . . . why? Ve vork to put goot pork on dinner tables . . . dot's vot!"

Max Lukas had made up his mind that Tenderlean sausage and bacon were foods he wanted to serve in his diners and restaurants. When he stated he'd order a thousand pounds of sausage a week, Stewart Williams blinked—but, Lukas continued, he could see certain problems that made substantial sausage orders a mixed blessing. Where, for instance, could the Tenderlean promoters find markets for the parts of a hog that were not used in the sausage? What about the heads, hocks and feet . . . the livers, loins and spareribs?

The Tenderlean project could not progress, Max Lukas explained, unless it had a sales program that kept the markets for its by-products neatly in balance with the demand for its specialties.

"Oh, we hadn't intended to get into the dressed-pork business," Carl explained. "Except on a sort of sample basis to show what our Tenderlean products were like. Isn't that right, Stewart?"

"That's the idea I had—but, gosh, when Mr. Lukas said he'd order a thousand pounds of sausage a week, he knocked the breath right out of me," Williams declared.

"We just wanted to show the restaurant and meat market owners that our kind of hogs made pork of extra-high quality," Ed Gaines explained. "Then we'd try to get them to ask their slaughterhouses for pork from Tenderlean pigs. We figured, first, we'd sell the pork buyers on the idea that our stuff is worth a premium . . . next, we'd convince some of the butchers that they could do more business by handling this quality of pork . . . and to get our top quality stock, we figured they'd be willing to pay the premium that it's worth."

Max Lukas shook his head. "Gentlemens, dot vill not vork. To a food buyer like me, nothing is special unless it comes right from the hands of the people who love it enough to make it special. From you, I buy Tenderlean pork—and pay extra to get it. From chust any butcher dot handles all kinds of pork —no, I vill not pay extra. You vill find ve are all the same, too, ve food buyers."

"But suppose we did produce sausage and bacon—or rather, that Stewart here processed it—what could he do with the rest of the cuts—the pigs' feet, for instance?"

"Vell," Max replied, "I came here maybe chust to buy sausage and bacon to make better breakfasts in my places, but now I see vot I better do. I better be your peegs' foot salesman. I buy your best, top, choice peegs a few at a time—the whole peegs after Mr. Villiams dresses them. I pay him to fix them for my orders. Maybe I find connections for the rest so I get as much sausage and bacon as I vant . . . ve see."

It was agreed that the Tenderlean producers would appoint a committee to select the best hogs available to supply Lukas and his customers; and Lukas would buy the hogs alive, paying the grower a 10 per cent premium above the Portland top market quotation. Then Lukas would pay Stewart Williams to butcher, process and truck the pork to its destination.

Within a week, the telephone in Stewart Williams' locker plant rang in the first call from Max Lukas . . . and from then on, a four o'clock call was a daily event. The "peegs' foot salesman" had found delicatessens that wanted tubs of pickled pigs' feet and hocks, boxes of fresh livers, cartons of head-cheese. He found a swank supper club that would make a specialty of small loin sections for barbecuing, and through the prestige of this, he promoted substantial orders for "bantam-size" loin roasts from independent meat shops that featured choice products. He manipulated his own orders for sausage and bacon to keep them in balance with the output of other products. Max found a market for ten hogs a day, then twenty, then thirty . . .

Stewart Williams enlarged his butchering facilities step by step. He increased the capacity of his refrigerators and bought a new truck to transport Tenderlean pork. Soon, however, the Tenderlean project was on the verge of outgrowing the capacity of his country abattoir and threatening to become so large that it would require the facilities of a real packing plant to service it efficiently. Word of this possibility spread across the prairie . . . and with live hogs selling at such fabulous prices, at twenty-five and twenty-six cents a pound, hog raising was infecting people with a fever such as they get in a gold rush.

Carl Yeoman heard the talk, and it worried him. So long as some of the prairie's farms produced a few hogs as a side line, grown economically on alfalfa pasture and small acreages of barley supplemented with some purchased protein concentrates, nobody was going to be seriously hurt if the bottom fell out of the Tenderlean project. Such farms would still have practically their normal specialties of wheat and marketable alfalfa hay. But now there was talk of farmers planning to make hog production their major enterprise.

The telephone calls from Max Lukas or his purchasing agent ordered more and more pork. "Gosh, take it easy," Stewart

Williams protested when Max relayed an order requiring the processing of thirty-five hogs in one day. "That's more than I can handle."

"Vell," Max replied, "tell all the Tenderlean experts I vill be at your plant tomorrow at one o'clock . . . and ve should haf vot they call a converence."

Stewart Williams passed his information on to Ed Gaines and Carl Yeoman. "Something's up," he prophesied. "Maybe Max wants to pull out—or push us in deeper."

Whatever the turn of events, Carl told himself, it was well to have it come soon, lest the brief, small splurge of success set them adrift on a current of optimism that would carry the whole Tenderlean enterprise over a waterfall of business difficulties.

To Carl's surprise, Max showed no sign of either reneging on his part in the project or of being impatient because operations could not expand faster. Instead, the food merchant was extremely congenial, and it became apparent that the purpose of his visit was to take stock of the whole Tenderlean proposition and make such plans as were wise and practical for continuing its progress.

As Carl listened, he was amazed at the information Max had accumulated concerning the character of the product he was handling. Max flicked through his file of orders and picked out copies on which he had scribbled notes. From these he described the shape, color, meat-and-fat proportions of loins, the cook-out quality of different sausage batches, the length of bacon strips and their variations in lean tissue. Max could put his finger on every occasion when the supply of strictly superior hogs was short and the marketing committee, in desperation, had filled the quota with some second-choice animals. Even more remarkable, however, were the observations Max recorded concerning the variations in size of the lean muscle in loin cuts that, from standpoint of weight, appeared to be remarkably uniform. Max showed paper tracings of the lean areas exposed on the ends of the loin roasts. The square inches of lean surface had been computed for each tracing, and as Max explained, these were really not very uniform because they varied from 3.1 to 5.4 square inches.

It was plain that Max was not presenting this information to condemn the Tenderlean products—in fact, there were times when he seemed to be bursting with enthusiasm. "You see, I know a lot about my Tenderlean peegs—and that's why I can sell this pork. But I tell you vot: Ve are chust too close to the limit of the really goot pork we can turn out. Now, gentlemens, ve have the problem to improve uniformity and raise our standards chust a little bit all the time. Vell, can ve do it?"

Can we do it? Carl didn't know it then, but this was an agribusiness question of profound importance. The Carl Yeoman that represented the present generation of Yeomans who had been agriculturists for centuries now found himself devoted to a new concept of his family's traditional vocation. The men sitting there in Stewart Williams' office—the food merchant, the processor, the hog grower, the supplier—all of them together were only the modern counterpart of Carl Yeoman's grandfather, Abner, the capable agriculturist of the earthbound era.

"I think we'd better hold some hefty conferences, don't you, Carl?" Ed Gaines was saying.

"It'll take a lot of brainwork to do what Max proposes—but I think it's the right way to proceed."

"To begin with, we need some expert advice on our breeding program," Ed said. "Take information about quality such as Max has collected; there ought to be some way to use it to improve our breeding stock."

"That's a research project—maybe we could get the State College or the experiment station people interested," Carl suggested.

"We need a steady supply of top stock," Stewart cautioned, "and to get it there'll have to be lots of pigs grown around here. But the interest is going to fall off unless you can think of ways to make good money from pigs that don't make the Tenderlean grade."

"Maybe we could develop a market for breeding stock," Ed proposed.

"Whatever we do, we must keep our sights on economical production," Carl warned.

"Say," Stewart exclaimed, "did you fellows see Johnson Brothers' ad in this week's paper. I got a copy hot off the press this morning." He spread the paper on the top of his desk and pointed to a full-page ad featuring machinery, but which included a boxed message carrying the headline ATTENTION HOG GROWERS. "They say our prairie isn't corn country, but we have obtained a shipment of hybrid seed corn that is adapted to our climate and soil. We believe you can grow 100-bushel yields on your irrigated acres. That's enough grain to feed out ten Tenderlean hogs per acre. How could you grow cheaper feed? Seed comes in ten-pound bags, enough to plant an acre. Price $2.00 per bag. Limit ten bags to a farm this season. Johnsons' invite you to try it!"

Carl flushed. "Well, I'll be dawgoned, now even my old rival, Ole Johnson, is getting in the Tenderlean boat with me!"

"Sure a lot of changes lately," Ed Gaines mused.

"A lot of changes since I left the farm," Stewart Williams echoed.

13.

DURING THE EARTHBOUND ERA, American agriculture clung to the basic security of subsistence farming . . . but the time came when the family farm's ability to provide a satisfactory standard of living depended on its capacity to give full and well-paid employment to the members of the family who, in other occupations, would be earning regular pay checks. Producing for family consumption on the farm was now of minor significance compared to the income received from the sale of the farm's products. The logical approach to bigger sales, bigger income, was through bigger production. The increase in farm production was accomplished all too quickly and too easily, with the result that such increased output created surpluses that depressed prices, and farmers came to the paradox that the better they farmed and the more they produced, the less might be the incomes they received.

The agribusiness era brought spectacular developments in off-the-farm supply, processing and marketing businesses as well as amazing progress in on-the-farm efficiency and productivity, but these developments burst upon us without our recognizing that they must be integrated and co-ordinated to produce the agribusiness counterpart of the prosperous, self-reliant, self-sufficient operations formerly consolidated in the way of life on a good homestead in the earthbound era. In our failure to understand the challenges of the transition from agriculture to agribusiness, we were not prepared to diagnose and treat the bumps and bruises that were bound to occur in the rough-and-tumble economic transformation that was taking place. In our ignorance of the real meaning of the commotion, we picked on the more conspicuous bruises which were showing up in relation to agriculture's surplus production and concluded that these were symptoms of an economic ailment that was strictly a farm problem.

American farming in the first half of the fifties has been poised between the forces of an expanding national economy and the weaknesses of a frustrated agricultural economy. This was the period in which our gross national product headed upward toward 300 and 400 billions. In five years the hourly wages of industrial workers climbed from $1.40 to $1.84 . . . and we had more than 60 million job holders. By 1955 the number of farm units had dropped below five million, of which about two million were commercial units . . . and these were busily producing surpluses of many crops and farm products. While the rest of the economy prospered, farming's income was jeopardized by the price-depressing effects of overproduction. Despite notable progress in production, the integration of farm policy with that of the business functions had not advanced sufficiently to provide strength essential to cope with the problems of balancing production and marketing.

In the agribusiness concept, the farmer is the man in the middle of the picture. In the fifties, he became the customer for businesses that sell him 16 billion dollars' worth of supplies . . . and the producer of 30 billion dollars' worth of products purchased by businesses serving as processors and distributors. These latter, in turn, add services and supplementary products in converting farm commodities into consumer items aggregating 75 billion dollars at retail level. If one adds to this the value of foods of marine origin, synthetic fibers and imported foods, the consumer bill increases to over 90 billion dollars. Thus both as a customer and as a supplier, the farmer's business stability is vital to the agribusiness structure.

The present status of the American farmer is so varied as to defy precise description. He's a man of extremes. In general, the commercial farmer is the owner and operator of a family farm which produces several thousands of dollars' worth of products for the market. On the other hand, about two million farmers operate at near subsistence levels, producing too little on their farms to provide good livings for their families through farm operations alone.

Midst all of this change, anyone having a stake in American farming during recent years had many things to ponder. Particularly so if one had a son who might seek his vocation in something as transitory as the agriculture of this period.

Carl and Hilda Yeoman proudly watched their red-haired son preside as toastmaster at the parents' banquet of the Future Farmers of America. David, now sixteen, was tall and slender— a youth at mid-point between boyhood and manhood. Boyishly, he grinned and blushed when he tangled himself in some of the program's details, but quick to recover his composure, he kept the proceedings rolling with manly poise and dignity.

"He's certainly in his element," Hilda whispered to Carl. Her husband nodded, but a very serious expression came over his face. Their son's element? What, exactly, were the implications of that thought? Did it mean that David was committed to farming as a lifetime occupation?

David was completing his third year in the high-school vocational agriculture course. Students taking this course are eligible for membership in the school's Future Farmers chapter. Their instructor serves as chapter adviser. The FFA member is active during the four years of his high-school studies but is expected to continue his association with his chapter for three years after graduation. There are 8,000 FFA chapters, with a total membership of about 380,000. FFA is set up with echelons of well-trained youthful officers at chapter, state and national levels—boys who can conduct organization affairs with the dignity, polish and adroitness that would do credit to their counterparts in any adult organizations, anywhere.

"It gives me great pleasure, as president of this chapter," David was saying, "to present our annual chapter farmer award to Henry Turner. Henry is completing his fourth year in vocational agriculture. He has specialized in a breeding hog project and in three years his gross income has amounted to $3,200. His records show a net income of $957 and he has an inventory of $545 in livestock and equipment. Our FFA program encourages members to establish savings from their projects, and Henry has invested $300 in savings bonds and also has $130 in a savings account at the bank. You've done a swell job, Henry, and we're proud to give you our chapter farmer award."

"Thank you very much, David," Henry said as he received the award plaque. "Guests and fellow Future Farmers, I accept this honor because I really want to go all the way in what it stands for—to be a real future farmer, and a good one."

Carl winced at the seriousness in the boy's voice . . . at the expression of respectful envy in his own son's eyes as Henry spoke. Hilda caught the flash of apprehension that had shown momentarily in Carl's face. "Don't be so serious," she whispered.

"This is serious business," Carl replied, but he put on a smile and applauded heartily while the dentist's son proudly showed his plaque to his parents.

The following evening Carl drove out to the farm to visit his mother. "Oh, I've heard such nice things about David," Betty Yeoman told her son. "The Turners said he handled the banquet wonderfully well. And wasn't it nice that Henry received the big prize?"

"It was quite an affair, Mother," Carl said. "Those kids have a lot on the ball. You'd be surprised how grown up they behave at a time like that." They visited a long time, the elderly, gray-haired lady eagerly listening to Carl's report of David's activities. "I think he's going to be a chip off the old block," she said as she rocked contentedly in her favorite wicker rocking chair. "But you've come to talk about something, Carl. What is it?"

Carl grinned. "You always know, don't you, Mother? Well, the subject is pretty close to the one we've been talking about —the youngsters who like farming. What I'd like us to talk about could have a lot to do with some young man's prospects of farming in the future." Then Carl explained that the problem on his mind was how best to arrange for the future transfer of ownership of the land now owned by his two sisters, his mother and himself.

"You see, Mother, if it is handed along in its separate parts through inheritance in the usual way, the farm will be broken up in pieces too small to make separate, efficient operating units. Or if one of the heirs should want to keep the farm together by buying out other heirs, he would face a staggering debt."

Carl explained that since the irrigation system had been installed the gross value of the farm's real estate had reached a figure of about $150,000. His mother gasped. "But, Carl, it wasn't long ago that I bought the Colton place for just $12,000 . . . and your dad and I bought the Bonner land for only $8,000."

"I know, Mother, but that was before we had irrigation on 250 acres. Those acres alone are worth four or five times as much as the dry land—and don't forget, that too has gone up in value quite a bit. We've had income as high as $15,000 in one year. Remember? But now suppose that the farm is inherited by the heirs of Sue and Meg and me—and David were the only one of them who wanted to hold on and operate the farm. To buy the other two thirds of the land, he'd have to pay off a debt of $100,000. But his one third of the land—even in our best year yet—gives him an income of only $5,000. Take his living out of that, and there'd hardly be a dollar left to pay off the debt. It's quite a problem, isn't it?"

"My goodness, Carl, I never thought of it that way," Betty exclaimed. "I wouldn't want my grandchildren to inherit a lot of mistakes if I can help it. Have you any suggestions, Carl?"

"The best plan I can think of to fit our situation is to form a corporation owned by the family."

"A corporation!" Betty exclaimed.

"Yes, we could incorporate—with Sue, Meg and I putting our land in the corporation along with yours. Then we would each hold shares of the corporation's stock in proportion to the property we transferred to the corporation as capital. Then the corporation would own the whole farm—and keep it together. If one of us wanted to sell some of our stock, we could do so if we had a buyer. But a change of ownership of the stock wouldn't take any acres out of the farm, which could happen now if one of my sisters or I sold some of the land we own."

"But who would run the farm . . ."

"Each share of stock would give its owner a vote, so the proposition that had the most shares of stock backing it would be the rule. The corporation could hire someone to operate the farm for a salary . . . or it could rent it same as we are doing now with Chet Burns. Instead of taking our rent in crops, however, the corporation would make the sales, pay its expenses, and pay its owners cash dividends. While the ownership of the farm would be held by the corporation, its operation would continue as a family farm . . . operated by and for our family. Incorporation would serve to keep the whole farm intact and avoid forcing a young farmer to go deep in debt."

"I'm glad one of the Yeomans has gained some experience in business; these things we're talking about sound more bewildering to me than mortgage terms, and heaven knows that they were complicated enough for me. Have you told your sisters about this idea?"

"Oh, no," Carl replied. "It would depend on what you thought about it first. I'll admit I've been pondering the idea for a long time, but what finally spurred me to speak to you about it was the program last night. I looked at Davy and Henry—both so eager and enthusiastic about farming. Of course, Henry may wind up being a dentist like his dad and David may become an engineer for a firm like Johnson Brothers. Who knows? But I thought to myself, now suppose either of these boys really wants to farm, how's he going to get started? Then it dawned on me that even in David's case there are really big problems. His inheritance would give him some land, yes, but it could also trap him in quite a predicament. I can see how the sentimental tie to the family's land—and that's a strong tie, believe me—could cause him to attempt something that could keep him hopelessly in debt for the best twenty or thirty years of his life."

"Oh, Carl, I surely wouldn't want that to happen," Betty said. "I've been thinking your grandfather would be so pleased if he could see how splendidly his old farm has been doing in the last five or six years—and I guess I've been dreaming, too, that Davy would someday step in and really make it a wonderful success—a modern version of the way it was in your grandfather's days."

"It'll never be the same, Mother—farming is business today as well as being a challenge to a man's energy and skills. This farm still has to grow—a lot, too—if it's going to make a good living for its operator. Look at Chet Burns. He and Dad had about 400 acres apiece when they began. Now Chet has the equivalent of 1,000 acres of his own, considering his irrigated land, and he rents the equivalent of nearly 1,500 acres from us —I mean, if you allow for the way irrigation increases our yields—and, while he's a very prosperous farmer, he's just about keeping in step with the earnings of a man in a first-class job. And I'll bet Chet has a capital investment of about $175,-000, too. The trouble is, Mother, farming's not up to par unless it can earn a good living for the operator's family as well as earn additional capital to increase the size of operations about one per cent a year."

"What does par mean?" his mother asked.

"That," Carl replied with a boyish grin, "is a pet idea of mine. I think there's such a thing as a par farm—and it's the only kind of farm worth having if farming people are to enjoy living standards as good as other people have."

His mother frowned. "But, Carl, every farm doesn't have a lot of good land—and very few of them around here can have irrigation. We have some dear old neighbors on the edge of the prairie who have always been hard up, as we say. They don't ask to be rich, but often they need help—higher prices, or easy loans, or something."

"Mother, I figure it's this way: Those who stay in farming need help to get started with a good unit. Those who can't do that need help to get away from the farm and into something else where they can be productive and earn a good living."

Betty Yeoman caught her breath. "Carl, you sound heartless. These people have made their homes on the same land for a lifetime. They don't know how to do anything but farm. You can't just drive them off. Mercy sakes, that would be a cruel thing to propose."

"Can't you just picture me organizing a caravan of hay trucks and a posse of prosperous farmers . . . going from one poverty farm to the next one . . . packing up all the hardship folks and shipping them out? Or should I organize a shotgun gang and march to the bank and order the tellers to shell out the money needed to make these marginal farms prosper? Or maybe I could make a career for myself in politics—hammering at Congress to pass laws that guarantee two million of them plenty of income at the expense of the taxpayers?"

"Don't say such ridiculous things!"

"Of course, Mother, I know this is a serious subject, but it bothers me that much as we know a problem like this exists, we do a mighty poor job of thinking of a good way to solve it. In the case of young couples who want to farm, we should help them get proper education and then find places for them on farms big enough to make fair livings. Those who can't do this will be better off in other employment where they can earn good pay. If they prefer rural living, they can live on small acreages and raise their families there. Of course, in the case of elderly farm couples who are on small farms, they will likely want to live out their lives there and should be encouraged to do so. Most of the adjustment to the new type of farming will be done by the new generation. I am sorry, Mother. I didn't intend to make a speech."

"I'm an old woman and I don't know how to solve economic problems," Betty replied. "I just know that it's a pity something nice doesn't happen for these humble, good, respectable neighbors."

"I think it's coming, Mother. A lawn mower factory is going to be established on a five-acre tract adjoining our company's warehouse. I'm on a Chamber of Commerce committee that helped promote its coming. There'll be jobs for one hundred when it opens—and it may grow enough to employ two or three hundred someday. The lawn mower company chose our prairie town for its factory site because it expects to recruit its workers from the so-called marginal farms in the foothills around the prairie."

"Well, I think that's a wonderful idea," Betty Yeoman enthused. Then her face clouded. "Was it cheap farm labor that attracted the factory owners?"

Carl grinned. "Nope. It's the capable workers they know they'll find around here that interests them. Fact is, the hours and wages are to be the same as for plants in the cities. So are the vacations and so-called fringe benefits. Farmers have a knack with machines—and making or assembling a power lawn mower is not much different to a farmer than making repairs on his mowing machine or keeping his old jitney in running order." Carl pulled a leaflet from his pocket. "In the words of the company's policy, 'The primary reason for placing our factories in rural communities is the availability of workers from surrounding farms—workers who are anxious to work in industry. At identical wage rates, hours and other conditions, we find that unit production costs are lower in our rural factories than in city plants.' In other words, Mother, there's a ready market for something called attitude-toward-the-job. Factory owners naturally like to find workers who believe in giving their employers a good day's work for their wages. Makes sense, doesn't it?"

"It even sounds exciting."

Carl picked up his hat and kissed his mother. "Past your bedtime, Mrs. Yeoman," he said.

"Mercy sakes, Carl, we haven't said a word about the pigs."

"Pretty good to escape from them once in awhile," Carl said, chuckling.

Ever since the day that Ed Gaines delivered David's birthday present—the sow named Princess—Carl Yeoman's life had become more and more involved in the prairie's pig enterprises. Always it seemed that one crisis was solved by creating a situation that produced another, a bigger crisis, and so on, until the whole program became extremely complicated. Driving home,

Carl mused about the number of people who had become involved in the Tenderlean pork enterprise since the time, seven years before, when he was worrying about the disposal of David's litter of baby pigs. He laughed aloud as he recalled the conferences—such serious conferences—he had had with the parents of the boys David said would like to join a 4-H pig club. Conferences! Carl considered trying to count them . . . a hundred, maybe . . . no, more likely a thousand.

Each conference was triggered by an idea that drew a group together, only to find that the counsel of someone outside the group was needed to provide the information or judgment on which progress could be based. What had begun as an effort of friends and neighbors to give their small problems a lift by their own bootstraps had grown like ripples in a pool, each new problem, each new idea, setting up an expanding ring of specialists, experts, scientists, business leaders. Carl chuckled at the thought of all these important people crowded around the old horse stall in his barn where Princess farrowed her first litter. What a lot of brains to deal with the destiny of a few little pigs, he thought.

Passing farms in the spring moonlight, Carl could glimpse the white hog houses that were there because of the chain of events that followed the birth of David's first pigs. The moonbeams sparkled on droplets of water flicked from sprinklers . . . sprinklers watering acres of foot-high corn . . . corn that came to the prairie because brains had been worked so diligently, planning improvements in the pig project.

Brains. A remarkable network of brains explained the extraordinary development of the Tenderlean program and all of its related projects, Carl reflected. Merely learning how to raise hogs—while it did take brains even to do that the best way—was only a small part of the know-how that was now involved in the prairie's pork-producing developments. Scientists in white coats in faraway laboratories were harnessing microscopic living creatures to produce molds which in turn formed chemical substances known as antibiotics that protect animal health and stimulate growth or more efficient use of feeds. That farm he just passed, Carl recalled, was running a check on a new adaptation of antibiotics in pig feeds, and one of the country's ablest scientists in the field of fermentation chemistry had visited that pigpen just a few weeks before. And a mile away, a representative of a big packing firm in Tokyo had picked out five young boars for shipment to Japan —because other able brains had helped design a breeding program here on the prairie that was attracting international attention. It was so simple, yet so complex, Carl mused. The trick was to forge a chain of brains that could deal with every proposition in the production of a pig and the preparation and delivery of its pork to the kitchens of consumers. It was a vertical integration of brainwork applying to a farm product from its start to the point where it was consumed . . . with due consideration, too, for all the human circumstances influenced by the product. Circumstances such as boys who want to become successful farmers . . . or weary old farmers who need good rural jobs to lift them out of the quagmire of hardships on their inefficient farms.

Sometimes the ideas that lead to intricate plans and complex operations can be launched with just a few words of common sense, Carl mused. Take the time the Tenderlean project had run into a wall of limitations, and it looked as if there was nothing left to do except retreat from all their ambitious ideas. Then Max Lukas had said, "Vell, when the pot roast doesn't sell for supper, ve put some of it in the beef stew for lunch. If that doesn't finish it, ve grind some more of it to make hash for breakfast. Ve di-wers-ify . . . and ve sell our beef." Diversity of operations was building the prairie a sound and expanding pig enterprise, Carl was thinking as he turned the car into his driveway.

It had taken a lot of planning and co-ordinating to develop this diversity which now took the form of specialized projects in the prairie's hog program. Originally, after the first flurry of interest in hogs—spurred, of course, by the high hog market of the late forties—the proposition had seemed so simple. Just multiply the numbers of their lean-meat stock and the customers would beat a pathway to their hog pens. To produce uniformly superior hogs, however, called for more knowledge than the prairie farmers possessed. When they solicited counsel from geneticists and livestock specialists, the Tenderlean program soon was in for drastic revision. The scientists said the breeding project needed a strain in which the essential characteristics had become fixed through a long process of selection and inbreeding; otherwise uniformity could not be established in stock that carried a variety of qualities drawn from several breeds mixed together the way Ed Gaines had blended them to create his Tenderlean stock. Skilled breeders of livestock were consulted, and they expressed grave doubts about the profits to be made in promoting a new breed as compared with the rewards that the same efforts would achieve if they were applied to established, widely known breeds.

The quest for useful suggestions caused Carl and Ed Gaines to consult Canadian livestock specialists because in Canada the progressive hog growers sell their hogs dressed instead of alive. This practice enables them to collect premium prices for pork of superior quality. Canadian farmers, college and experiment station livestock specialists and meat packers had joined forces in designing a practical program that would yield pork of superior quality to compete for export trade with England. Their studies had established preference for an English breed known abroad as the Large White, a name that was changed to Yorkshire in Canada. The Dominion's farmers were alert to the recommendations developed from the extensive studies of the profitable qualities of hog breeds, and soon more than 90 per cent of Canada's hogs were Yorkshires. The postwar quest for leaner pork in the United States caused American breeders to import many Canadian Yorkshires, and by the time Carl and Ed Gaines were conducting their investigations the Yorkshire breed was on the verge of a boom in this country. The fact that Ed's Tenderlean stock carried Yorkshire blood verified the lean-pork qualities of this white breed.

When the prairie's Tenderlean enthusiasts settled into conferences about their breeding program, their consultants strongly advised them to establish some registered Yorkshire herds. They pointed out that, first, the introduction of pure-bred Yorkshire blood in Tenderlean stock would improve the uniformity of the commercial stock, and, second, the production of registered Yorkshire breeding stock, which was rapidly gaining in popularity, would add a new source of income to the prairie's hog enterprises. In comparison to the difficulties of establishing a pedigree registration service for a new breed and the expense of promoting sale of the little-known Tenderlean breed, participating in the established registry and promotional activities of the Yorkshire organization had many advantages, the livestock specialists counseled.

Acting on this advice, ten of the prairie's livestock farmers formed the Tenderlean Yorkshire Associates and founded herds, individually owned, but registered in the name of the group. Thus they consolidated their advertising in promoting what appeared to be a single breeding unit. The Associates supplied choice young stock for the 4-H and FFA members to grow in their pig projects, and subsequently provided an excellent market through which the youngsters could sell their pigs when they were grown to optimum value. In addition to supplying purebred stock to upgrade the prairie's commercial breeding herds, the Associates held three auction sales annually which attracted hog breeders within a radius of a thousand miles. Sales in February and August featured registered bred gilts and a sale in October offered young boars of breeding age. Whereas the best live hog prices received in the original Tenderlean operations ranged between twenty and twenty-eight cents per pound, the Associates sold their choice purebreds at figures amounting to thirty to fifty cents per pound—and sometimes an exceptional boar or gilt sold as high as $200 to $500.

A second group of the prairie's hog farmers formed the Tenderlean Commercial Breeders Association. Their herds had been founded on Ed Gaines's Tenderlean stock and they used purebred Yorkshire boars purchased from the Associates to upgrade their product. Not being purebred and registered, their stock had no appeal to the purebred breeder. The commercial breeders castrated the male pigs in their litters and sold them as weanlings, to be fed out to market weight by farmers who did not care to keep female stock and bother with the birth and starting of baby pigs. Some butcher stock producers, however, preferred to buy bred gilts and raise the small pigs instead of buying them. To serve these farmers, the commercial breeders kept their best sow pigs, grew them to breeding age, and sold them just before they were ready to have their pigs.

With these sources of good stock near at hand, most of the prairie's farmers grew butcher hogs. Some grew only a few

222

to utilize cull or waste produce and to supply home-grown pork for their freezers; others grew as many as several hundred annually. These growers of butcher stock formed a cooperative auction market association, the Tenderlean Pork Producer's Co-operative, and rented the county fairgrounds' hog barn to use as a pavilion for its weekly sales.

One of the services of the Pork Producer's Co-operative was selection of a weekly quota of the choicest market hogs for Max Lukas. For a time, all of these were processed locally by Stewart Williams, but Max gradually expanded the merchandising of Tenderlean pork until it was necessary to truck shipments of live hogs weekly to two other country abattoirs in the region. The premium of 10 per cent above the week's top market for butcher hogs which Max paid for the stock that qualified for his trade kept all participants in the Tenderlean program on their toes to share in this bonus. Even the producers of the elite breeding stock, the Tenderlean Yorkshire Associates, had a real stake in the bonus for superior pork received through the merchandising efforts of Max Lukas. Every pig in the prairie's Tenderlean enterprises was weighed, measured, graded and evaluated from birth to meat counter or breeder's barnyard. From this mass of performance data, the breeders were able to identify the boars that transmitted superior qualities to the pigs they sired. This information helped them select the families or bloodlines that produced superior stock; helped them eliminate those which slowed up progress toward higher standards of efficiency in growth or quality of the dressed pork. Even the farmer who bought a feeder pig for home-grown pork could be shown how many pounds of feed that pig's family required, on the average, to produce a pound of live hog at market size; how many days were required to reach the 200-pound weight; the average figures for length of carcass, thickness of back fat, area of lean in a pork chop; average percentage of dress-out and of the primal cuts, which included bacon sides, shoulders, hams and loins. If he wanted to do so, the farmer could also find out how many baby pigs were born, how many survived to weaning age and how much the pigs weighed when thirty-five days old in the average litter born in the hog family from which his pig was descended. While this intricate array of facts did not directly interest the man who grew a butcher hog, it did, indeed, have a great deal to do with making the prairie's Tenderlean program capable of improving the results and satisfactions the hog grower and the pork consumer ultimately received.

Outsiders began to notice the way the prairie people had become absorbed with the subject of pork—superior pork. Any stranger who ventured into one of Main Street's barbershops for a haircut was destined to hear a strange jargon of animal husbandry terms instead of so much of the usual banter about ball games, bird hunting and politics. Smart salesmen calling on local merchants soon learned to intersperse reports of the popularity of Tenderlean products with the snappy stories they picked up on their itineraries. The tourist waiting while the oil was changed in his motor was pretty sure to resume his journey with more facts about pigs and pork than he'd ever imagined anybody knew. The prairie had, indeed, become pork-conscious.

The consultations and conferences arranged by the Tenderlean producers in their quest for information and advice began to serve a double purpose. Not only did they encompass the know-how of pork production and marketing that benefited the prairie's participants, but now they were also attracting visitors from afar who were interested in studying the data the Tenderlean producers were accumulating. County agents brought caravans of livestock farmers to the prairie for tours of the Tenderlean facilities. Scientists came in groups to study the mass of records relating to genetics and nutrition. Associations of butchers, restaurant owners and home economists scheduled their meetings in the town's hotel so that their members might get a first-hand impression of "a noteworthy new development" in the once commonplace product known as pork. Even the big packing firms sent representatives of their sales and buyer staffs to have a look at something they politely called "unique and interesting." Little by little, the Tenderlean producers began reciprocating, with their own store of knowledge freely given in return for the counsel and suggestions they received from an ever-expanding circle of consultants.

"Seems to me a new kind of thinking prevails here on the prairie," Kirk McGregor, the newspaper editor, told Ed Gaines as he interviewed the hog breeder concerning one of the conferences on the Tenderlean project. "I don't hear much griping about a farm problem any more. In fact, you farmers are talking in business terms."

"We hope we've gotten over the foolishness of producing hogs and then worrying about what to do with them," Ed replied.

"Aren't a lot of these conferences devoted to 'worrying,' as you call it?"

"In a way, yes. But around here the farmer's thinking doesn't stop at the chute where his hogs are loaded into a buyer's truck; now he's thinking all the way to the dining tables of pork customers. You can call it 'business talk'—but our business, as we see it now, is to create a good, big, sound business enterprise all the way from pigpen to dining table."

"You're trying to make the economic pie bigger rather than just cutting the present pie in a different way. Is that it?"

"Yep, that's the idea," Ed declared.

In a nutshell, that's the challenge in using the agribusiness idea.

14.

THE COURSE OF this discussion and the story used to illustrate it in terms of human reactions and experiences might lead the reader to the ludicrous conclusion that agriculture's problems would vanish if every farmer enrolled in the Tenderlean pork project and lived up to the specifications set forth by Carl Yeoman and his associates. Of course, no such hypothesis is intended. In order to simplify a proposition that has a myriad of complexities for each and every farm product to which it might be applied, we have used an "allegory of the pigs" . . . hoping in this way to give the reader an outline which, in his own thinking, he can adapt to any kind of farming and all the off-farm businesses related to it.

We have in this allegory of the pigs the application of an idea

—an idea that challenges individuals and groups to use their initiative in developing successful business operations for every phase of producing and servicing a product that originates on the farm. To make these operations successful, those who engage in agribusiness must be everlastingly in quest of versatile, better and more appealing ways to market agricultural products. Successful agribusiness creates a prosperous agribusiness economy . . . a boon to that large part of the population engaged in agribusiness in one way or another, and a significant factor in improving our living standards and our over-all prosperity.

Little by little we can win the battle of the farm problem by developing successful agribusiness programs for each type of farming or each farm product. There is no simple and easy formula for accomplishing this . . . no master plan to be handed down from the top. Instead, the agribusiness idea assists in perception of the scope of business problems and opportunities existing in the farm-to-market perspective of anything agriculture can produce. This comprehension of the integrated relationship of agriculture and business helps private enterprise direct its efforts in making sounder, faster progress toward a prosperous, expanding economy. In so doing, we reduce the pressures that push us toward further reliance on government programs. Consequently, even those of us who are not engaged in any of the agribusiness enterprises have good reason to wish that the agribusiness idea would influence our national agricultural policy. The so-called farm problem—which, as Congressional attention signifies, is of widespread public interest—has much more promise of solution through the constructive development of agribusiness than through legislation to control and subsidize farm crops.

Referring again to the allegory of the Tenderlean pigs, caution has been exercised to avoid letting our story of agribusiness achievement become a fantasy of improbable success. To reassure the reader, a look at the figures supplied by the Grocery Manufacturers of America reveals that market baskets throughout America are daily being filled with more and more food products that match or surpass our Tenderlean pork story in successful application of the agribusiness idea. Dollar sales of food at retail grew from 10.2 billion dollars in 1939 to 43.7 billion in 1955. Part of this increase was due to dollar inflation, but using 1947–49 as base 100, the tonnage has risen from 72 in 1939 to 131 in 1955. Population has increased considerably, of course, but much of the increase in tonnage and considerably more of the increase in dollar volume is credited to the development of new types of foods—particularly the "convenience foods" with built-in chef and maid service.

Then, consider the fabulous increase in frozen foods as reported by the National Frozen Food Distributors Association. As recently as 1949, the per capita consumption of frozen foods was 17 pounds. In 1954 it was 41 pounds and in 1955 the score was 45 pounds—up nearly 10 per cent. One of the interesting agribusiness developments in connection with frozen foods is the great increase of brand merchandising of farm products. There was no brand, and not much uniformity of quality from day to day, when the grocer sold a pound of spinach out of the basket a grower filled in the field . . . or the butcher sold a pork chop off a carcass hanging in his cooler. Now, however, when these foods are packaged for freezing, they are labeled with brand names, the purpose and value of which are to denote quality to the buyer. Quality standards and uniformity then become tremendously important in com-

229

peting for sales through intensive advertising and skillful merchandising. So our allegory of the Tenderlean brand of pork is not the least bit farfetched.

Nor is it unlikely that crop land may shift to new uses, as suggested in the Tenderlean allegory of agribusiness. American farming's investment in research to find new uses for present crops or new crops to replace those plagued with overproduction and low prices is pathetically skimpy . . . yet American industry sets aside about 2 per cent of gross sales to use for research and development leading to new and better products and new and larger markets. Meager as is our research to find business-building uses for farm crops, we have progressed far enough to realize that the possibilities exist. Sooner or later we may use our abundance of cereal grains to make fuels, building materials, paper, rubber and plastics. We may introduce new fiber crops to make paper, textiles and plastics. We may discover that chemicals, medicines and household products of great variety can be extracted from strange or common plants that can be grown profitably by farmers who have participated effectively in using the agribusiness idea.

Carl Yeoman looked up at the calendar that hung above his cluttered desk in his small office off the salesroom of the Prairie Farm Supply Company. Saturday, March 31, 1956. He glanced at his wristwatch—ten minutes past one—and listened to make sure the footsteps near the outer door of the salesroom were not those of another last-minute customer. He recognized they were Charlie Plant's. He heard Charlie set the lock, then his voice: "See you Monday, Carl." He answered cheerily, "Have a nice week end, Charlie." Carl reached across his desk and tore the March sheet from the big calendar. Rougher every week now, he told himself. Being situated close to the lawn mower factory was good for business—too good. Nearly every one of the hundred and fifty employees in the factory was a die-hard farmer of sorts, and the advent of spring brought them flocking to Carl's salesroom for seeds, fertilizers, weed killers, chick starter, brooders, fence posts and paint. First paint some of them have bought in twenty-five years, Carl mused. But that's the difference between living on a so-called farm with too little income and living in the same place with a factory job that pays good wages, he was thinking.

"March thirty-first!" Carl exclaimed.

This was the day that David would come home from college for his spring vacation. Carl scrambled into his gabardine jacket. He made a pass at straightening up the clutter on his desk top and picked up the money pouch he would drop in the bank's deposit slot on the way home. Outside, the air was fresh and crisp, free from the peculiar odors of agricultural chemicals and the mild irritant of feed and fertilizer dusts. A robin fluffed out his feathers, chirped saucily and flew from the top of Carl's pickup to an insulator on the crossbar of a telephone pole.

Passing through the suburban blocks, Carl grinned as he noted the men from offices and shops busily raking lawns, languidly posing on spade handles, obediently crawling across flowerbeds while a wife with a sweater draped over her shoulders pointed at spots where caution must be exercised to respect the safety of sprouting daffodils and tulips. Carl imagined he could scent the earthy odor of fresh-turned soil, the mild, sweet fragrance of buds ready to open in a profusion of flowers and leaves. A farmer at heart, every one of them, Carl thought.

There was a fenderless, lilac-colored monstrosity parked in front of the Yeoman residence. The "It"—Carl recalled—the 1935 jalopy Henry Turner and David had jointly purchased

231

and remodeled for something like thirty dollars, in defiance of the more orthodox and less adventuresome railroad fare of twenty-five dollars it would have cost each of them to travel back to college last September.

David, his red hair trimmed in a scalp-hugging "butch," was a size and a half bigger than Carl remembered him. As he gripped his son's firm hand, Carl wondered if, in his own twentieth year, he had as much of the ruggedness manhood is made of. Hilda, bustling between kitchen and dining table, pressured them into the formalities of washing and seating themselves for lunch.

"Say, Wise One, there are some questions I want to ask," David said when he had finished second helpings of everything Hilda offered.

"Don't be flip with your father," Hilda remonstrated.

"No offense," David replied. "He is the oracle of wisdom for the things on my mind."

"My stock advice is to keep your mind on your books, young man," Carl stated.

"And I respectfully use a little of it . . . every day." David grinned. "But here's the setup: I'm finishing my junior year in the college of agriculture, majoring in animal husbandry, but I could make a switch and get a degree in ag engineering or ag economics—specializing in agricultural business administration. Now, the question is: Which is the best course to take?"

"Is your interest in livestock slipping?" Carl asked.

"No, I wouldn't say that. When I was younger, I was sure I wanted to start out farming on my own. But, gosh, Dad, farming is sick most of the time, it seems to me. Right now the country's all het up about the farm problem—and everybody's holding his breath to see what Congress will do about it. Is it always going to be like that?"

232

"Frankly, I don't know, David."

"Well, tell me, Dad, are the farmers here on the prairie depending on Uncle Sam to keep them from poverty?"

"I think all of them would resent that idea—but the situation here is an unusual one, thanks to our Tenderlean business and the lawn mower factory."

"But didn't the bust in the hog market last summer hurt the Tenderlean business pretty severely?"

"Oh, it hurt all right. But every kind of business runs into difficulties one time or another. Too many hogs; too low a price. Just the same, the hog producers here squared off and kept their operations on a sound basis . . . even made progress in some respects."

"Well, Dad, why was a hog producer here on the prairie in any different circumstances than hog farmers in the rest of the United States?"

"I don't want my answer to sound smug, David, but it's like this: We've learned how to make business decisions from start to finish in pork production. Any farmer around here, if he keeps his ears open, doesn't just dive blindly into growing a lot of hogs. We measure our opportunities from the dining tables back to the pigpen, back to the land that grows the feed and the expenses for supplies and equipment. Every step in our program calls for decisions—decisions based on the best business judgment we can muster."

"You do it the hard way. Why not convince Congress that hogs should bring twenty cents a pound and let it go at that?"

"Then who'd bother to improve pork so that consumers would want more and more of it? And if bureaucrats are going to make all the decisions for the hog farmers, pretty soon our farmers would be like peasants—wards of the economy who lived in a humble state of security without any of the privileges or opportunities enjoyed in relying on their own initiative. I'm sure the farmers here like to make their own decisions, but they've learned to make them in a strong alliance with other business people who have a part in the destiny of our pork business."

"Does what you're saying mean that that smart cookie, Max Lukas, saw a way to make a boodle of dough selling your fancy pork? And he made a better market for the prairie's pigs than other hog-producing regions have had."

"I certainly do mean that Max proved to be a smart businessman—and, for that matter, every hog grower around here has arrived at the point of view that he'd like to see Max get rich on Tenderlean pork. When Max shows up in a new Cadillac, we're all glad to see it because, to us, it means our business is thriving. In a way, Max is key man in a business proposition that is bringing almost a million dollars of income to the prairie."

"Gosh, that's a lot of dough!"

"You mentioned the drop in hog prices last year. In general, it cut prices right in half. But our income wasn't hurt as much as that—thanks to Max and some others. We put on a drive and increased the market for our premium stock by nearly twenty per cent. We sharpened up on operations all along the line—producing at less cost, concentrating on fewer but better stock, raising our standards, and getting set to give our problems and our competition a rough time trying to hold us back."

"Decisions again?"

"Hundreds of decisions—all of them made with our eyes on a target of producing and merchandising a better pork product."

David stood up, stretched to his full six feet, thrust his hands deep in his trouser pockets and paced stiff-legged to the dining-room window. Hilda came from the kitchen and took the lunch cloth from the table. She looked admiringly at the broad shoulders of her son, and with a saucy toss of her head she said, "Look at the two of you . . . Yeoman, the name is . . . cultivators of the land, it's supposed to mean . . . and there's some beautiful sunshine outdoors and a garden that needs some spading . . ."

"Mother, Mother, don't you realize the country is suffering from the overproduction of agriculture? Dad and I are just helping the Secretary of Agriculture get production under control again—at no cost to the taxpayers, mind you."

"Dear me, such heroes," Hilda scoffed.

"Well, Dad, you speak as if a fellow could make a pretty good thing of it growing livestock in the right place at the right time."

"There's more to it than growing the stock, David. I'm becoming convinced that farming is an incomplete part of a bigger unit. It's somewhat like a factory that makes bolts. The bolts have to be produced in the right size, type and quantity to match the machines that use bolts or else the bolt factory will have a tough time staying in business. So I'm pretty sure the bolt makers study the needs of the machine manufacturers and the material suppliers so that they know what to make and how much to turn out. Fit that idea to farming and you have a more satisfactory outlook, haven't you?"

"Yeah," David muttered. "But my farm management course indicates that a farmer nowadays has to stretch out and operate on a pretty big scale to be efficient. How does he do it except by muscling in somehow and expanding all he can?"

"Like in any other occupation, David, a fellow has to decide which he wants to do: take a job he can get or set up in business for himself; work for a specified pay check or take his chances on making more or less by going on his own."

"That's what I'm coming to—should I complete some technical training and take a job when I finish college, or should I aim to go farming on my own?"

"Well, to set up a comparison, let's consider the job you might take—what's it like?"

"Oh, some of the big equipment companies are scouting the colleges for engineering graduates, offering jobs at starting pay up to five thousand a year and even more. Some are looking for grads in the ag engineering field, for which I could qualify."

"What kind of figures would these jobs average in, say, the next twenty-five years?"

"The company people tell us they should average better than ten thousand. Or let's say a capable fellow could reach that figure by the time he's had ten years' experience."

"Well, David, it would take quite a farm to match income such as that."

"In my course in economics, we learned that forty per cent of the country's five million farmers produced ninety per cent of our agricultural products. The farms in this group averaged sixty-eight thousand dollars capital. Their average gross income, in round figures, was fifteen thousand, and average expenses were ten thousand—leaving an average residual income for family labor, management and investment of five thousand."

"It would take a ten-dollar profit on five hundred hogs a year to equal those figures, David."

"Gosh, Dad, do many farms on the prairie grow that many hogs?"

"No, David, very few of them do—and while the decision

is up to the individual, we would not want to encourage anyone to dive into the pig business in a big way. We base our
operations on a program that keeps a neat balance between the
specialists who produce hogs for all or most of their income
and the others who produce stock to diversify their farms or
as small projects, such as the boys in 4-H and FFA and the rural
families who now have jobs in the lawn mower plant."

"But if somebody makes a profit on a Tenderlean pig project, Dad, what's to keep him from plunging in more and
more?"

"Nothing—except some lessons in business caution that seem
to work. We produced a small amount of something way better than ordinary pork—and it brought us premium prices. Instead of making our super-quality product common by producing a lot of it without improving it constantly, we have
continually raised our standards so that the supply of superior
pork stays in balance with the demand our merchandising system creates. We apply the same type of selective program to
both the butcher stock and the purebred stock produced for
breeding purposes. So, in order to make the most profit, our
producers stay in line with the program. And don't forget, our
standards are set high, too, on equipment, on feeding methods
and on management. Anybody is welcome to try to fit himself
into our system by demonstrating he can 'carry the ball,' but
he can't just barge in and get the benefits of this program by
producing a lot of ordinary hogs in a slap-happy fashion. You
see, the farmers exercise guidance over the program through
their own association to which all good producers belong."

"But don't you want this Tenderlean program to expand?"

"Sure we want it to expand—and as fast as possible. But, Son,
if we've learned anything from our pork experience around
here, we've learned that supplier and producer and marketer

must perform like a good football team so that we don't goof-up our progress. There'll be a lot of changes—and one of these days our expansion may astonish all of us."

The lad drew a deep breath and turned to his father. "How old will I be when it happens, Dad?"

"At your age I wanted to build Rome in a day, too, but I had to outwit a depression for quite a few years before I could hope to buy anything but my own groceries. But to get back to livestock farming—we're making sound progress and even now there are signs that big packers are getting quite interested in our prairie hogs. If we expand on a sound basis, it's possible a real packing plant would be established here. That's one of the possible changes. Our best producers are demonstrating that they can make more income out of pork than they can growing price-supported wheat. If our marketing program continues to expand, some of them may be growing hogs on a mass-production scale same as the prairie's biggest farms grow wheat now. I suspect the day may come when we'll be designing hog farms that are so efficient one man can feed out five thousand hogs at a time. Of course, it won't be easy. There will be years of hard going and not everyone will make the grade."

"Automation comes to the pigpen!" David exclaimed.

"Could be."

"Dad, that kind of farm would need a million dollars capital."

"It would require a lot of capital—and that's another place where the decisions we've mentioned are very important. We've been careful to emphasize the financial aspects of the Tenderlean program. We discourage a kid's growing one pig if he's going to try it on a shoestring. Someday the credit needs of this pork program may be really big—but as that day approaches, we aim to be able to show bankers and investors that we have a sound proposition."

"Got anybody that would back a fellow named David Yeoman—about three years from now, after I graduate and finish my military service?"

"On the old homestead?"

"On Yeoman Acreage, Incorporated," David answered with a grin. "You know I'm an interested stockholder, thanks to the ten shares Grandmother left me."

"It was your grandmother's fondest dream that someday you would farm the family's land."

"Well, I'm sure glad it's still all in one piece. Your idea about forming a family corporation, Dad, looks like a good one now."

"There have been many problems, Son, but all in all it seems to be working out satisfactorily. But we still have the big problem of accumulating enough capital to set up our own operations."

The boy rubbed his hands over his close-cropped red hair. "How much capital does our corporation need?"

Hilda came from the kitchen and sat in a chair across the table from her husband. She folded her hands on the table top and looked quizzically from son to father.

"Am I breaking in on a corporation caucus?"

"Oh, we'll let you in without your showing your credentials," David said.

"Well, Son," Carl continued, "we could say the farm itself is worth a hundred and fifty thousand and it ought to pay its stockholders four per cent on that amount. Our rental arrangement with Chet Burns pays that very handily—but it's not a permanent proposition because the day is not far off when Chet will retire. And if our corporation sets up its own operations, isn't it reasonable that it should have enough capital to finance enterprises that will net its managing operator ten thousand a year while the earnings on total capital continue at four per cent or better?"

"Ten thousand a year!" David exclaimed.

"Why not? If the manager has enough on the ball to make himself a ten-thousand-dollar job in an industry related to farming, why not in farm operations, too?"

"That's quite a challenge, Dad."

"Sure it is—but if you're serious about wanting to farm, your challenge is to learn how to plan and manage a farming enterprise well enough to do it. That's the way businesses off the farm develop jobs that pay that kind of money."

"Man, you really believe agriculture is in for a change!"

"In agriculture, in the old days, David, you produced most of your supplies; you produced most of your family's food; you traded off most of the produce you had left over ready for consumption. That's all behind us. Today we have agribusiness—a compound of farming and the businesses that supply farms and process and distribute their products. Farming must stand shoulder to shoulder with its related businesses. In other words, we put the farmer in a business suit. See what I mean?"

"And the challenge is to live and help others to live on higher standards than past generations have experienced," Hilda added.

"What you mean is: Fill the horn of plenty for everybody— isn't that the idea, Dad?"

"Yes, David, that is the idea. And it will take millions of agribusiness-like decisions made day after day by tens of thousands of businessmen and farmers to get the job done. In that way we not only can make farming as prosperous as the rest of the economy but also we can help raise the living standard of America in general by making wiser use of our expanding capital to produce and use food and fiber in the manner that will give us the greatest satisfaction," Carl Yeoman replied.

"Mom, do you suppose one of those suits would fit me?"

"What suit, David? Oh, I get it—you mean you want to be the farmer in a business suit." His mother looked across the table and read an answer in her husband's eyes. "I believe a Yeoman could wear that suit with pride . . . and distinction, David."

A Note about the Authors

DR. JOHN H. DAVIS *served as Assistant Secretary of Agriculture in President Eisenhower's first administration and was also president of the powerful Commodity Credit Corporation in Washington. Two years ago he moved to Harvard, where the Graduate School of Business Administration was launching a major effort to reshape American thinking about the nation's agriculture. The core of this effort has been the new concept of agribusiness worked out by Dr. Davis. He has served as member or chairman of many United States delegations to international food and agricultural conferences. He comes from Missouri.*

KENNETH HINSHAW *has been editing and writing for farm journals since 1928. He is now in charge of publications and public relations for Eastern States Farmers' Exchange, a cooperative handling an $80,000,000 volume of farm supplies every year. He lives in Springfield, Massachusetts.*